To be read aloud
in that cozy dining
room at #1711.—

May joy go with
it — to the "General",
and Lady Atkinson
is the wish of the
Widdy J——

The
Lady of the Decoration

The
Lady of the Decoration

By
Frances Little

New York
The Century Co.
1907

THE DE VINNE PRESS

TO ALL
GOOD SISTERS, AND TO MINE
IN PARTICULAR

The Lady of the Decoration

The Lady of the Decoration

SAN FRANCISCO, July 30, 1901.

My dearest Mate:

Behold a soldier on the eve of battle!
I am writing this in a stuffy little hotel
room and I don't dare stop whistling
for a minute. You could cover my
courage with a postage stamp. In the
morning I sail for the Flowery Kingdom, and if the roses are waiting to
strew my path it is more than they have
done here for the past few years.

When the train pulled out from home
and I saw that crowd of loving, tear-

ful faces fading away, I believe that
for a few moments I realized the ac-
tual bitterness of death! I was leaving
everything that was dear to me on
earth, and going out into the dark unknown, alone.

Of course it's for the best, the disagreeable always is. You are responsible, my beloved cousin, and the con-
sequences be on your head. You
thought my salvation lay in leaving
Kentucky and seeking my fortune in
strange lands. Your tender sensibil-
ities shrank from having me exposed
to the world as a young widow who
is not sorry. So you "shipped me
some-wheres East of Suez" and tied
me up with a four years' contract.

But, honor bright, Mate, I don't believe in your heart you can blame me
for not being sorry! I stuck it out
to the last,—faced neglect, humilia-

4

tions, and days and nights of anguish, almost losing my self-respect in my effort to fulfil my duty. But when death suddenly put an end to it all, God alone knows what a relief it was!

And how curiously it has all turned out! First my taking the Kindergarten course just to please you, and to keep my mind off things that ought not to have been. Then my sudden release from bondage, and the dreadful manner of it, my awkward position, my dependence,—and in the midst of it all this sudden offer to go to Japan and teach in a Mission school!

Is n't it ridiculous, Mate? Was there ever anything so absurd as my lot being cast with a band of missionaries? I, who have never missed a Kentucky Derby since I was old enough to know a bay from a sorrel! I guess old Sister Fate does n't want me to be a one part star. For eighteen years I played pure comedy, then tragedy for seven, and now I am cast for a character part.

Nobody will ever know what it cost me to come! All of them were so terribly opposed to it, but it seems to me that I have spent my entire life going against the wishes of my family. Yet I would lay down my life for any one of them. How they have stood by me and loved me through all my blind blunders. I'd back my mistakes against anybody else's in the world!

Then Mate there was Jack. You know how it has always been with Jack. When I was a little girl, on up to the time I was married, after that he never even looked it, but just stood by me and helped me like a brick. If it had n't been for you and for him I should have put an end to myself long ago. But now that I am free,

6

The Lady of the Decoration

Jack has begun right where he left off seven years ago. It is all worse than useless; I am everlastingly through with love and sentiment. Of course we all know that Jack is the salt of the earth, and it nearly kills me to give him pain, but he will get over it, they always do, and I would rather for him to convalesce without me than with me. I made him promise not to write me a line, and he just looked at me in that quiet, quizzical way and said: "All right, but you just remember that I'm waiting, until you are ready to begin life over again with me."

Why it would be a death blow to all his hopes if he married me! My widow's mite consists of a wrecked life, a few debts, and a worldly notion that a brilliant young doctor like himself has no right to throw away all his chances in order to establish a small hospital for incurable children. Whenever I think of his giving up that long-cherished dream of studying in Germany, and buying ground for the hospital instead, I just gnash my teeth.

Oh! I know that you think it is grand and noble and that I am horrid to feel as I do. Maybe I am. At any rate you will acknowledge that I have done the right thing for once in coming away. I seem to have been a general blot on the landscape, and with your help I have erased myself. In the meanwhile, I wish to Heaven my heart would ossify!

The sole power that keeps me going now is your belief in me. You have always claimed that I was worth something, in spite of the fact that I have persistently proven that I was not. Don't you shudder at the risk you are taking? Think of the responsibility of

standing for me in a Board of Missions!
I 'll stay bottled up as tight as I know
how, but suppose the cork *should* fly?

Poor Mate, the Lord was unkind
when he gave me to you for a cousin.

Well it 's done, and by the time you
get this I will probably be well on my
sea-sick way. I can't trust myself to
send any messages to the family. I
don't even dare send my love to you.
I am a soldier lady, and I salute my
officer.

ON SHIP-BOARD. August 8th, 1901.

It 's so windy that I can scarcely
hold the paper down but I 'll make the
effort. The first night I came aboard,
I had everything to myself. There
were eighty cabin passengers and I
was the only lady on deck. It was very
rough but I stayed up as long as I

could. The blue devils were swarming so thick around me that I did n't want to fight them in the close quarters of my state-room. But at last I had to go below, and the night that followed was a terror. Such a storm raged as I had never dreamed of, the ship rocked and groaned, and the water dashed against the port-holes; my bag played tag with my shoes, and my trunk ran around the room like a rat hunting for its hole. Overhead the shouts of the captain could be heard above the answering shouts of the sailors, and men and women hurried panic-stricken through the passage.

Through it all I lay in the upper berth and recalled all the unhappy nights of the past seven years; disappointment, heartache, disillusionment, disgust; they followed each other in silent review. Every tender memory

10

and early sentiment that might have lingered in my heart was ruthlessly murdered by some stronger memory of pain. The storm without was nothing to the storm within, I felt indifferent as to the fate of the vessel. If she floated or if she sank, it was one and the same to me.

When morning came something had happened to me. I don't know what it was, but my past somehow seemed to belong to someone else. I had taken a last farewell of all the old burdens, and I was a new person in a new world.

I put on my prettiest cap and my long coat and went up on deck. Oh, my dear, if you could only have seen the sight that greeted me! It was the limpest, sickest crowd I ever encountered! They were pea-green with a dash of yellow, and a streak of black under their eyes, pale around the lips

11

and weak in their knees. There was only one other woman besides myself who was not sick, and she was a missionary with short hair, and a big nose. She was going around with some tracts asking everybody if they were Christians. Just as I came up she tackled a big, dejected looking foreigner who was huddled in a corner.

"Brother, are you a Christian?"

"No, no," he muttered impatiently. "I'm a Norwegian."

Now what that man needed was a cocktail, but it was not for me to suggest it.

At table I am in a corner with three nice old gentlemen and one young German. They are great on story-telling, and I've told all of mine, most of yours and some I invented. One of the old gentlemen is a missionary; when he found that I was distantly connected

12

with the fold he immediately called me
"Dear Sister". If I were at home I
should call him "Dear Pa", but I am
on my good behavior.

The eating is fairly good, only sometimes it is so hot with curry and spice
that it nearly takes my breath. My
little Chinese waiter is entirely too solicitous for my comfort. No amount
of argument will induce him to leave
my plate until I have finished, after a
few mouthfuls he whisks it away and
brings me another relay. After press-
ing upon me dishes of every kind, he
insists on my filling up all crevices
with nuts and raisins, and after I have
eaten, and eaten, he looks hurt, and
says regretfully: "Missy sickee, no
eatee."

There is one other person, who is
just as solicitous. The little German
watches my every mouthful with round

solemn eyes, and insists upon serving everything to me. He looks bewildered when anyone tells a funny story, and sometimes asks for an explanation. He has been around the world twice, and is now going to China for three years for the Society of Scientific Research. He seems to think I am the greatest curio he has yet encountered in his travels.

The chief excitement of our trip so far has been the day in Honolulu. I wanted to sing for joy when we sighted land. The trees and grass never looked so beautiful as they did that morning in the brilliant sunshine. It took us hours to land on account of the red tape that had to be unwound, and then there was an extra delay of which I was the innocent cause. The quarantine doctor was inspecting the ship, and after I had watched him examine the emigrants, and had gotten my feelings wrought up over the poor miserable little children swarming below, I found a nice quiet nook on the shelter deck where I snuggled down and amused myself watching the native boys swim. The water on their bronze bodies made them shine in the sunlight, and they played about like a shoal of young porpoises. I must have stayed there an hour, for when I came down there was considerable stir on board. A passenger was missing and we were being held while a search of the ship was made. I was getting most excited when the purser, who is the sternest and best looking man you ever saw, came up and pounced upon me. "Have you been inspected?" he demanded, eyeing me from head to foot. "Not any more than at present," I answered meekly. "Come with me," he said.

I asked him if he was going to throw

me overboard, but he was too full of
importance to smile. He handed me
over to the doctor saying: "Here is
the young woman that caused the delay." Young woman, indeed! but I
was to be crushed yet further for the
doctor looked over his glasses and said:
"Now how did we miss that?"

But on to Honolulu! I don't wonder
people go wild over it. It is as if all
the artists in all the world had spilled
their colors over one spot, and Nature
had sorted them out at her own sweet
will. I kept wondering if I had died and
gone to Heaven! Marvelous palms,
and tropical plants, and all hanging in
a softly dreaming silence that went to
my head like wine.

I started out to see the city, with
two old ladies and a girl from South
Dakota, but Dear Pa and Little Germany joined the party. Oh! Mate

how I longed for you! I wanted to tie
all those frousy old freaks up in a hard
knot and pitch them into the sea! The
girl from South Dakota is a little better than the rest, but she wears a
jersey!

There *are* real tailor-made people on
board, but I don't dare associate with
them. They play bridge most of the
time and if I hesitated near them I'd
be lost. I'll play my part, never fear,
but I hereby swear that I will not
dress it!

STILL ON BOARD. August 18th.

Dear Mate:

I am writing this in my berth with
the curtains drawn. No I am not a bit
sea-sick, just popular. One of the old
ladies is teaching me to knit, the short-
haired missionary reads aloud to me,

the girl from South Dakota keeps my
feet covered up, and Dear Pa and
Little Germany assist me to eat.

The captain has had a big bathing
tank rigged up for the ladies, and I
take a cold plunge every morning. It
makes me think of our old days at the
cottage up at the Cape. Did n't we
have a royal time that summer and
were n't we young and foolish? It
was the last good time I had for many
a long day—but there, none of that!

Last night I had an adventure, at
least it was next door to one. I was
sitting up on deck when Dear Pa came
by and asked me to walk with him.
After several rounds we sat down on
the pilot house steps. The moon was
as big as a wagon wheel and the whole
sea flooded with silver, while the flying
fishes played hide and seek in the shadows. I forgot all about Dear Pa and

was doing a lot of thinking on my own account when he leaned over and said:

"I hope you don't mind talking to me. I am very, very lonely." Now I thought I recognized a grave symptom, and when he began to tell me about his dear departed, I knew it was time to be going.

"You have passed through it," he said. "You can sympathize."

I crossed my fingers in the dark. "We are both seeking a life work in a foreign field—" he began again, but just here the purser passed. He almost stumbled over us in the dark and when he saw me and my elderly friend, he actually smiled!

Don't you dare tell Jack about this, I should never hear the last of it.

Can you realize that I am three whole weeks from home? I do, every second of it. Sometimes when I stop to think what I am doing my heart almost bursts! But then I am so used to the heartache that I might be lonesome without it; who knows?

If I can only do what is expected of me, if I can only pick up the pieces of this smashed-up life of mine and patch them into a decent whole that you will not be ashamed of, then I will be content.

The first foreign word I have learned is "Alohaoe", I think it means "my dearest love to you." Any how I send it laden with the tenderest meaning. God bless and keep you all, and bring me back to you a wiser and a gladder woman.

KOBE. August 18th, 1901.

Actually in Japan! I can scarcely believe it, even with all this strange

life going on about me. This morning
a launch came out to the steamer
bringing Miss Lessing and Miss Dixon,
the two missionaries in whose school
I am to work. When I saw them, I
must confess that my heart went down
in my boots! Theirs must have done
the same thing, for we stood looking
at each other as awkwardly as if we
belonged to different planets. The
difference began with our heels and
extended right on up to the crown of
our hats. Even the language we spoke
seemed different, and when I faced the
prospect of living with such utter
strangers, I wanted to jump overboard!

My fellow passengers suddenly became very dear, I clung to everything
about that old steamer as the last link
that bound me to America.

As we came down the gang plank, I
was introduced to "Brother Mason"

and "Brother White", and we all came ashore together. I felt for all the world like a convict sentenced to four years in the penitentiary. When we reached the Hotel, I fled to my room and flung myself on the bed. I knew I might as well have it out. I cried for two hours and thirty-five minutes, then I got up and washed my face and looked out of the window.

It was all so strange and picturesque that I got interested before I knew it. By and by Miss Lessing came in. Now that her hat was off I saw that she had a very sweet face with pretty dark hair and a funny little twinkle behind her eyes that made me think of you. She told me how she had come out to Japan when she was a young girl, and how she had built up the school, and all she longed to do for it. Then she said, "Your coming seems like the direct answer to prayer. It has been one of my dearest dreams to have a Kindergarten for the little ones, it just seems too good to be true!" And she looked at me out of her nice shining eyes with such gratitude and enthusiasm that I was ashamed of what I had felt.

After that Miss Dixon came up and they sat and watched me unpack my trunk. It took me about two minutes to find out that they were just like other women, fond of finery and pretty things and eager for news of the outside world. They examined all the dainty under clothes that sister had made for me, they marvelled over the high heeled slippers, and laughed at the big sleeves.

"Where are you going to wear all these lovely things?" asked Miss Dixon. And again my heart sank, for even my simple wardrobe, planned for

23

the exigencies of school life, seemed strangely extravagant and out of place.

But I want to say right now, Mate, that if I stay here a thousand years I'll never come to jerseys and eight-year-old hats! I am going to subscribe to a good fashion paper, and at least keep within hailing distance of the styles.

It is too warm to go down to the school yet so we are to spend a week in the mountains before we start in for the fall term.

Dear Pa and Little Germany have been here twice in three hours but I saw them first.

Home letters will not arrive until next week, and I can scarcely wait for the time to come. I keep thinking that I am away on a visit and that I will be going back soon. I find myself saving things to show you, and even starting

24

to buy things to bring home. I have a good deal to learn, have n't I?

HIEISAN. August 28th, 1901

Fairy-land, real true fairy-land that we used to talk about up in the old cherry-tree at grandmother's! It 's all so, Mate, only more bewitching than we ever dreamed.

I have been in little villages that dropped right out of a picture book. The streets are full of queer, small people who run about smiling, and bowing and saying pretty things to each other. It is a land where everybody seems to be happy, and where politeness is the first commandment.

Yesterday we came up the mountains in jinrikishas. The road was narrow, but smooth, and for over three hours the men trotted along, never halting or changing their gait until we stopped for lunch.

There is not much to a Japanese house but a roof and a lot of bamboo poles, but everything is beautifully clean. Before we had gotten down, several men and women came running out and bowing and calling "Ohayo, Ohayo" which means "good-morning." They ran for cushions and we were glad enough to sit on the low benches and stretch ourselves. Then they brought us delicious tea, and gathered around to see us drink it. It seems that light hair is a great curiosity over here, and mine proved so interesting that they motioned for me to take off my hat, and then they stood around chattering and laughing at a great rate. Miss Lessing said they wanted me to take my hair down, but would not ask it because of the beautiful arrangement. Shades of Blondes! I wish you could have seen it! But you *have* seen it after a hard set of tennis.

When we had rested an hour, and drunk tea, and bowed and smiled, we started out again, this time in a kind of Sedan chair, made of bamboo and carried on a long pole on the shoulders of two men. Now I have been up steep places but that trip beat anything I ever saw! I felt like a fly on a bald man's head! We climbed up, up, up, sometimes through woods that were so dense you could scarcely know it was day-time, and again through stretches of dazzling sunshine.

Just as I was beginning to wonder what had become of our luggage, we passed four women laughing and singing. Two of them had steamer trunks on their heads, and two carried huge kori. They did not seem to mind it in

the least, and bowed and smiled us out
of sight.

Another two hours' climb brought us
to this village of camps called Hieisan.
There are about forty Americans here,
who are camping out for the summer,
and I am the guest of a Dr. Waring
and his wife from Alabama.

My tent is high above everything, on
a great overhanging rock, and before
me is a view that would be a fit setting
for Paradise. This mountain is sacred
to Buddha, and the whole of it is thick
with temples and shrines, some of them
nobody knows how old.

I have been trying to muster courage
to get up at three o'clock in the morning to see the monkeys come out for
breakfast. The mountains are full of
them, but they are only to be seen at
that hour.

There are some very pleasant people
here, and I have made a number of

friends. I am something of a conundrum, and curiosity is rife as to *why* I came. Mrs. Waring dresses me up and shows me off like a new doll, and the women consult me about making over their clothes.

I don't know why I am not perfectly miserable. The truth is, Mate, I am having a good time! It's nice to be petted and treated like a child. It is good to be among plain, honest people, that live out doors, and have healthy bodies and minds.

I want to forget all that I learned about the world in the past seven years. I want to begin life again as a girl with a few illusions, even if they are borrowed ones. I know too much for my years and I'm determined to forget.

The home letters were heavenly. I've read them limber. I'll answer the rest to-morrow.

The Lady of the Decoration

At last after my wanderings I am settled for the winter. The school is a big structure, open and airy, and I have a nice room facing the west where you dear ones are. On two sides tower the mountains, and between them lies the magical Inland Sea. This is a great naval and military station, and while I write I can hear the bugle calls from the parade grounds.

I have a pretty little maid to wait on me and I wish you could see us talking to each other. She comes in, bows until her head touches the floor and hopes that my honorable ears and eyes and teeth are well. I tell her in plain English that I am feeling bully, then we both laugh. She is delighted with all my things, and touches them softly

30

saying over and over: "It's mine to care for!"

There are between four and five hundred girls in the school and, until I get more familiar with the language, I am to work with the older girls who understand some English. You would smile to see their curiosity concerning me. They think my waist is very funny and they measure it with their hands and laugh aloud. One girl asked me in all seriousness why I had had pieces cut out of my sides, and another wanted to know if my hair used to be black. You see in all this big city I am the only person with golden tresses, and a green carnation would not excite more comment.

Yesterday we went shopping to get some curtains for my room. Such a crowd followed us that we could scarcely see what we were doing. When we went into the stores we sat on the floor and a little boy fanned us all the time we were making our selection.

Monday, Miss Lessing asked me to begin a physical culture class with the larger girls who are being trained for teachers, so I decided that the first lesson would be on *skipping*. It is an unknown art in Japan and the lack of it makes the Kindergarten work very awkward.

I took fourteen girls out on the porch and told them by signs and gestures to follow me. Then I picked up my skirts, and whistling a coon-song, started off. You never saw anything to equal their look of absolute astonishment! They even got down on their hands and knees to watch my feet. But they were game, and in spite of their tight kimonas and sandalled feet they made a brave effort to follow. The first attempt was disastrous, some fell on their faces, some went down on their knees, and all stumbled. I did n't dare laugh for the Japanese can stand anything better than ridicule. I helped and encouraged and cheered them on to victory. The next day there was a slight improvement, and by the third day they were experts. I found that they had spent the whole afternoon in practice! Now what do you suppose the result is? An epidemic of skipping has swept over Hiroshima like the measles! Men women and children are trying to learn, and when we go out to walk I almost have convulsions at the elderly couples we pass earnestly trying to catch the step!

I was so encouraged by this success that I taught the girls all sorts of steps and figures, even going so far as to teach them the *quadrille*! But my am-

bition led me a little too far. One day
I came to class with a brand new step,
which I had invented myself. It *was*
rather giddy, but a splendid exercise.
Well I headed the line and after the
girls had followed me around the room
twice I saw that they were convulsed
with laughter! When I asked what
was the matter, they explained between
gasps that the step was the principal
movement in the heathen dance given
during festivals to the God of Beauty!
My saints! Would n't some of my
dear brethren do a turn if they knew?

Every afternoon I take about forty
of the girls out for a walk. Our favorite stroll is along the moat that sur-
rounds the old castle. It is almost always spilling over with lotus blossoms.
The maidens, trotting demurely along
in their rain-bow kimonas and little
clicking sandals make a pretty picture.
We have to pass the parade grounds

of the barracks where 20,000 soldiers are stationed, and I do wish you could see them trying to be modest, and yet peeping out of the corners of their little almond eyes in a way which is not peculiar to any particular country.

And the way they imitate me makes me afraid to breathe naturally. This thing of being a shining example is more than I bargained for. It is one of the few things in my checkered career that I have hitherto escaped.

Never mind Mate, I could n't be frivolous if I wanted to down here. Kobe would have proven fatal, for there are many foreigners there, and the temptation to have a good time would have been too much for me. I am rapidly developing into a hymn-singing sister, and the world and the flesh and the devil are shut up in the closet. Let us pray.

The Lady of the Decoration

October 2nd, 1901.

At last, dear Mate, I am started at my own work with the babies and there are n't any words to tell you how cunning they are. There are eighty-five high class children in the pay kindergarten, and forty in the free. The latter are mostly of the very poor families, most of the mothers working in the fields or on the railroads. There are so many pitiful cases that one longs for a mint of money and a dozen hands to relieve them. One little girl of six comes every day with her blind baby brother strapped on her back. She is a tiny thing herself and yet that baby is never unstrapped from her back until night comes. When I first saw her old weazened face and her eagerness to play, I just took them both in my lap and cried!

The Lady of the Decoration

One funny thing I must tell you about. From the first week that I got here, the children have had a nickname for me. I noticed them laughing and nudging each other on the street and in the school, and whenever I passed they raised their right hands in salute, and gave a funny little clucking sound. They seemed to pass the word from one to another until every youngster in the neighborhood followed the trick. My curiosity was aroused to such a pitch that I got an interpreter to investigate the matter. When he came to report, he smilingly touched my little enamelled watch, the one Jack gave me on my 16th birthday, and apologetically informed me that the children thought it was a decoration from the Emperor and they were saluting me in consequence! And they have named me "The Lady of the Decoration". Think of it, I have a title, and I am actually looked up to by these funny yellow babies as a superior being. They forget it some time though when we all get to playing together in the yard. We can't talk to each other, but we can laugh and romp together, and sometimes the fun runs high.

I am busy from morning until night. The two kindergartens, a big training class in physical culture, two Japanese lessons a day and prayers about every three minutes, don't leave many spare hours for homesickness. But the longing is there all the same, and when I see the big steamers out in the harbor and realize that they are coaling for *home,* I just want to steal aboard and stay there.

The language is something awful. I get my tongue in such knots that I have to use a corkscrew to pull it straight again. Just between you and me, I have decided to give it up and devote my time to teaching the girls to speak English instead. They are such responsive, eager little things, it will not be hard.

As for the country, I would n't dare to attempt a description. Sometimes I just *ache* with the beauty of it all! From my window I can see in one group banana, pomegranate, persimmon and fig trees all loaded with fruit. The roses are still in full bloom, and color, color everywhere. Across the river, the banks are lined with picturesque houses that look out from a mass of green, and above them are teahouses, and temples and shrines so old that even the moss is gray, and time has worn away the dates engraved upon the stones.

We spent yesterday at the sacred Island of Miyajima, which is about one hour's ride from here. The dream of it is still upon me and I wish I could share it with you. We went over in a sampan, a rude open boat rowed by two men in undress uniform. For half an hour we literally danced across the sea; everything was fresh and sparkling, and I was so glad to be alive and free, that I just sang for joy. Miss Lessing joined in and the boatmen kept time, smiling and nodding their approval.

The mountains were sky high, and at their base in a small crescent-shaped plain was the village with streets so clean and white you hated to walk on them. We stopped at the "House of the White Cloud" and three little maids took off our shoes and replaced them with pretty sandals. The whole house was of cedar and ebony and bamboo and it had been rubbed with oil

until it shone like satin. On the floor
was a stuffed matting with a heavy
border of crimson silk, and in the corner of the room was a jar that came
to my shoulder, full of wonderfully
blended chrysanthemums. All the
rooms opened upon a porch which hung
directly above a roaring waterfall, and
below us a dozen steps away stretched
the sparkling sea, full of hundreds of
sailing vessels and junks.

In the afternoon, we wandered over
the island, visiting the old, old temples,
listening to the mysterious wailing of
the wind bells, feeding the deer and
crane, and drinking in the beauty of it
all. I felt like a disembodied spirit,
traveling back, back over the centuries,
into dim forgotten ages. The dead
seemed close about me, yet they
brought no gloom, for I too was dead.
All afternoon I had the impression of

41

trying to keep my consciousness from drifting into oblivion through the gate of this magical dream!

How you would enjoy it all, and read its deeper meaning, which is hidden from me. But even if I can't philosophize like a certain blessed old Mate of mine, I can *feel* until every nerve is a tingle with the thrill.

Good bye for a little while; I 've stolen the time to write you this, and now it behooves me to hustle.

November 12th, 1901.

It 's been a long while between "drinks", but I have been waiting until I could write a letter minus the groans. The truth is I have hit bottom good and hard and it is only to-day that I have come to the surface. When the exhilaration of seeing all the new

42

and strange sights wore off, I began to sink in a sea of homesickness that threatened to put an end to the kindergarten business for good and all.

I worked like mad, and all the time I felt like one of these whizzing rockets that go rushing through the air and die out in a miserable little fizzle at the end. I can stand it in the daytime, but at night I almost go crazy. And you have no idea how many women do lose their minds out here. Nearly every year some poor insane creature has to be shipped home. You need n't worry about that though, if I had mind enough to lose I 'd have lost it long ago. But to think of all my old ambitions and aspirations ending in the humble task of wiping Little Japan's nose!

I suppose you think I am pulling for the shore but I am not. I am steering my little craft right out in the billows.

It may be dashed to smithereens, and it may come safely home again, but in any case, I 'll have the consolation of the Texas cowboy that "I 've done my durndest!"

By the way, what has become of Jack? He need n't have taken me so literally as never to send me a message even! You mentioned his having been at the Cape while you were there. Was he just as unsociable as ever? I can see him now lying flat on his back in the bottom of a boat reading poetry. I hate poetry, and when he used to quote his favorite passages I made parodies on them. Now *you* were always different. You 'd rhapsodize with him to his heart's content.

Just here I had a lovely surprise. I looked out of the window and saw a coolie pull a little wagon into the yard and begin to unload. I could n't imagine what was taking place but pretty soon Miss Dixon came in with both arms full of papers, pictures, magazines and letters. It was all my mail! I just danced up and down for joy. I guess you will never know the meaning of letters until you are nine thousand miles from home. And such dear loving encouraging letters as mine were! I am going to sit right down and read them all over again.

November 24th, 1901.

Clear sailing once more, Mate! In my last, I remember, I was blowing the fog horn pretty persistently.

The letters from home set me straight again. If ever a human being was blessed with a good family and good friends it is my unworthy self!

The Lady of the Decoration

The past week has been unusually exciting. First we had a wedding on hand. The bride is a girl who has been educated in the school, so of course we were all interested. Some time ago, the middle-man, who does all the arranging, came to her father and said a young teacher in the Government school desired his daughter in marriage. The father without consulting the girl investigated the suitor's standing, and finding it satisfactory, said yea. So little Otoya was told that she was going to be married, and the groom elect was invited to call.

I was on tiptoe with curiosity to see what would happen, but the meeting took place behind closed doors. Otoya told me afterwards that she had never seen the young man until he entered the room, but they both bowed three times, then she served tea while her mother and father talked to him.

The Lady of the Decoration

"Did n't you talk to him at all?" I asked. She looked horrified. "No, that would have been most immodest!" she said. "But you peeped at him," I insisted. She shook her head, "That would have been disgrace." Now that was three months ago and she had n't seen him until Monday when they were married.

At our suggestion they decided to have an American wedding and I was appointed mistress of ceremonies. It was great fun, for we had a best man, besides brides-maids and flower girls, and Miss Lessing played the Wedding March for them to enter. The arrangements were somewhat difficult owing to the fact that the Japanese consider it the height of vulgarity to discuss anything pertaining to the bride or the wedding. They excused me on the ground that I was a foreigner.

The affair was really beautiful!

The Lady of the Decoration

The little bride's outer garment was the finest black crepe, but under it, layer after layer, were slips of rainbow tinted cob-web silk that rippled into sight with every movement she made. And every inch of her trousseau was made from the cocoons of worms raised in her own house, and was spun into silk by her waiting maids.

After the excitement of the wedding had subsided, we had a visitation from forty Chinese peers. They came in a cavalcade of kuramas, gorgeously arrayed, and presenting an imposing appearance. I ran for the poker for I thought maybe they had come to finish "Us Missionaries." But, bless you, they had heard of our school and our kindergarten and had come for the Chinese Government to investigate ways and means. They made a tour of the school, ending up in the kindergarten. The children were completely overpowered by these black-browed, fierce-looking gentlemen, but I put them through their paces. The visitors were so pleased that they stayed all morning and signified their unqualified approval. When they started to leave, I asked the interpreter if their gracious highnesses would permit my unworthy self to take their honorable pictures.

Would you believe it? Those old fellows puffed up like pouter pigeons, and giggled and primped like a lot of school girls! They stood in a row and beamed upon me while I snapped the kodak. If the picture is good, I 'll send you one.

This morning I had to teach Sunday School. I 'll be praying in public next. I see it coming. The lesson was "The Prodigal Son", a subject on which I ought to be qualified to speak. The

The Lady of the Decoration

Japanese youths understood about one word out of three, but they were giving me close attention. I was expounding with all the earnestness in me when suddenly I remembered a picture Jack used to have. It was of a lean little calf tearing down the road, while in the distance was coming a lazy looking tramp. Underneath was the legend:

> "Run, bossy, run,
> Here comes the Prodigal Son."

That settled my sermon, so I told the boys a bear story instead.

How I should love to drop in on you to-night and sit on the floor before the fire and pow-wow! I 'll be an awful back number when I come home, but just think how entertaining I 'll be! I have enough good dinner stories to last through the rest of my life!

For heaven's sake send me some hat pins, nice long ones with pretty heads.

50

The Lady of the Decoration

And if you are in New York this winter please get me two bottles of that violet extract that I always use.

My dearest love to all, and a hundred kisses to the blessed children at home. Don't you *dare* let them forget me.

November 27th, 1901.

I told you it would come! My prophetic soul foresaw it. I had to lead the prayer in chapel this morning. And I play the organ in Sunday School and listen to two Japanese sermons on Sunday.

I tell you, Mate, this part of the work goes sadly against the grain. They say you get used to hanging if you just hang long enough, so I suppose I 'll become reconciled in time.

You ask me *why* I do these things. Well you see it 's all just like a big

51

work shop, where everybody is working hard and cheerfully and yet there is so much work waiting to be done, that you don't stop to ask whether you like it or not.

I can't begin to tell you of the hopelessness of some of the lives out here. Just think of it! Women working in the stone quarries, and in the sand pits and on the railroads, and always with babies tied on their backs, and the poor little tots crippled and deformed from the cramped position and often blind from the glare of the sun.

What I am crazy to do now is to open another free kindergarten in one of the poorest parts of the city. It would cost only fifty dollars to run it a whole year, and I mean to do it if I have to sell one of my rings. It is just glorious to feel that you are actually helping somebody, even if that somebody is a small and dirty tribe of Japanese children. I get so discouraged and blue sometimes that I don't know what to do, but when a little tot comes up and slips a very soiled hand into mine and pats it and lays it against his cheek and hugs it up to his breast and says, "Sensei, Sensei," I just long to take the whole lot of them to my heart and love them into an education!

They don't know the word love but they know its meaning, and if I happen to stop to pat a little head, a dozen arms are around me in a minute, and I am almost suffocated with affection. One little fellow always calls me "Nice boy" because that is what I called him.

We are having glorious weather, cold in doors but warm outside. The chrysanthemums and roses are still blooming, and the trees are heavily laden with fruit. The persimmons grow bigger than a coffee cup and the oranges are tiny things, but both are delicious. Chestnuts are twice as big as ours, and they cook them as a vegetable.

You 'll be having Thanksgiving soon, and you will all go up to Grandmother's, and have a jolly time together. Have them fix a plate for me, Mate, and turn down an empty glass. Nobody will miss me as much as I will miss my poor little self.

What jolly Thanksgivings we have had together! The gathering of the clans, the big dinner, and the play at night. Not exactly a play, was it, Mate? More of a vaudeville performance with you as the stage manager, and I as the soubrette. Do you remember the last reunion before I was married? I mean the time I was Lady Macbeth and gave a skirt dance, and you did lovely stunts from Grand Opera. Have you forgotten Jack's famous parody on "My Country 'Tis of Thee?"

> "My turkey, 'tis of thee,
>   Sweet bird of cranberry,
>   Of thee I sing!
>   I love thy neck and wings,
>   Legs, back and other things," etc, etc.

There goes the bell, and here go I. I can appreciate the feelings of a fire engine!

Christmas Day, 1901.

Had somebody told you last Christmas, as we trimmed the big tree and made ready for the family gathering, that this Christmas would find me in a foreign country teaching a band of little heathens, would n't you have thought somebody had wheels in his head?

The Lady of the Decoration

And yet it is true, and I have only to lift my eyes to realize fully that I am really in the flowery kingdom. The plum blossoms are in full bloom and the roses too, while a thick frost makes everything sparkling white in the sunshine. The mountains have put on a thin blue veil trimmed in silver, and over all is a turquoise sky.

And best of all, everybody—I speak figuratively—is happy. It may be that some poor little waif is hungry, having had only rice water for breakfast, it may be some sad hearts are beating under the gay kimonas, and it *may* be, Mate dear, that somebody, a stranger in a strange land, can't keep the tears back, and is longing with all her mind and soul and body for home and her loved ones. But never you mind, nobody knows it but you and me and a bamboo tree!

The Lady of the Decoration

This afternoon we are going to have tea for the Mammas and Papas, and I am going to put on my prettiest clothes and do my yellow locks in their most fetching style.

I shall lock up tight, way down deep, all heartaches and longings and put on my best smile for these dear little people who have given to me, a stranger, such full measure of their sympathy and friendship, who, in the big service last month, when giving thanks for all the great blessings of the past year, named the new Kindergarten teacher first.

Do you wonder that I am happy and miserable and homesick and contented all at the same time?

The box I sent home for Christmas was a paltry offering compared to what I wanted to send, but the things were bought with the first money I ever earned. They are packed in so tight with love that I doubt if you ever get them out.

Our Christmas dinner was not exactly a success. We invited all the foreigners in Hiroshima, twelve in number, and everybody talked a great deal and laughed at everybody's stale jokes, and pretended to be terribly hilarious. But there was a pathetic droop to every mouth, and not a soul referred to *home*. Each one seemed to realize that the mere mention of the word would break up the party.

I tell you I am beginning to look with positive reverence on the heroism of some of these people! Tears and regrets have no place here; desire, ambition, love itself is laid aside, and only taken out for inspection perhaps in the dead hours of the night. If heart breaks come, as come they must, there is no crying out, no rebellion, just a stiffer lip and a firmer grip and the work goes on.

I wish I was like that, but I 'm not. If Nature had put more time on my head and less on my heart, she would have turned out a better job.

I put a pipe in the box for Jack. If you think I ought not to have done it, don't give it to him. As old Charity used to say, "I don't want to discomboberate nobody." Only I hope he won't think I am ungrateful and indifferent.

NAGASAKI. January 14th, 1902.

Now are n't you surprised at hearing from me in Nagasaki? I am certainly surprised at being here! One of the teachers at the school, Miss Dixon, was taken sick and had to come here to see a doctor. I was lucky enough to be asked to come with her.

I am so excited over being in touch with civilization again that I can't sleep at night! The transports and all the steamers stop here, and every type of humanity seems to be represented. This morning when I went out to mail a letter, there were two Sheiks in uniform in front of me, at my side was a Russian, behind me two Chinamen and a Japanese, while a Frenchman stepped aside for me to pass, and an Irishman tried to sell me some vegetables!

Miss Dixon had to go to the Hospital for a few days, though her trouble is nothing serious, and I accepted an invitation from Mrs. Ferris, the wife of the American Consul, to spend a few days with her.

The Lady of the Decoration

And oh! Mate, if you only *knew* the time I have had! If I were n't a sort of missionary-in-law I would quote Jack and say it has been "perfectly damn gorgeously." If you want to really enjoy the flesh-pots just live away from them for six months and then try them!

The night I came, the Ferrises gave me a beautiful dinner, and I wore evening dress for the first time in two years, and was as thrilled as a debutante at her first ball! It was so good to see cut glass and silver, and to hear dear silly worldly chatter that I grew terribly frivolous. Plates were laid for twenty, and who do you suppose was on my right? The severe young purser who was on the steamer I came over in! His ship is coaling in the harbour and he is staying with the Ferrises, who are old friends of his. He is so solemn that he almost kills me. If he were n't so good looking I could let him alone, but as it is I can't help worrying the life out of him.

The dinner was most elaborate. After the oysters, came a fish nearly three feet long all done up in sea-weed, then a big silver bowl was brought in covered with pie-crust. When the carver broke the crust there was a flutter of wings, and "four and twenty black birds" flew out. This it seems was done by the Japanese cook as a sample of his skill. All sorts of queer courses followed, served in the most unique manner possible.

After dinner they begged me to sing, and though I protested violently, they got me down at the piano. I did n't get up any more until the party was over for they made me sing every song

The Lady of the Decoration

I knew and some I did n't. I sang some things so hoary with age that they were decrepit! The purser so far forgot himself as to ask me to sing "My Bonnie lies over the Ocean"! I did so with great expression while he looked pensively into the fire. Since then I have called him, "My Bonnie," and he *hates* me.

The next day we went out to services on board the battleship "Victor." The ship had been on a long cruise and we were the first American women the officers had seen for many a long day. They gave us a rousing welcome you may be sure. Through some mistake they thought I was a "Miss" instead of a "Mrs." and I shamelessly let it pass. During service I heard little that was said for the band was playing outside and flags were flying and I was feeling frivolous to the tip of my toe!

The Lady of the Decoration

I guess I am still pretty young, for brass buttons are just as alluring as of old.

When the Admiral heard I was from Kentucky, he invited us to take tiffin with him, and we exchanged darkey stories and the old gentleman nearly burst his buttons laughing. After tea, he showed us over the ship, making the sailors line up on deck for our benefit.

"Tell the band to play 'Old Kentucky Home'," he ordered.

"You 'll lose a passenger if you do!" I cried, "for one note of that would send me overboard!"

He was so attentive that I had little chance to talk to the young officers I met. But several of them have called since, and I have been out to a lot of teas and dinners and things with them.

The one I like best is a young fellow from Vermont. He is very clever and jolly and we have great fun together. In fact, we are such chums that he showed me a picture of his fiancée. He is very much in love with her, but if I were in her place I would try to keep him within eye-shot.

We will probably go home to-morrow as Miss Dixon is so much better. I am glad she is better, but I could have been reconciled to her being mildly indisposed for a few days longer.

I forgot to thank you for the kodak book you sent Christmas; between the joy of seeing all the familiar faces, and the bitterness of the separation, and the absurdity of your jingles, I nearly had hysterics! I almost felt as if I had had a visit home! The old house, the cabin, the cherry tree, and all the family even down to old black Charity, the very sight of whom made me hungry for buckwheat cakes, all, all gave me such joy and pain that it was hard to tell which was uppermost.

It 's worth everything to be loved as you all love me, and I am willing to go through anything to be worthy of it. I have had more than my share of hard bumps in life, but, thank Heaven, there was always somebody waiting to kiss the place to make it well. There is n't a day that I have n't some evidence of this love; a letter, a paper, a book that reminds me that I 'm not forgotten.

A note has just come from his Solemn Highness, the purser, asking me to go walking with him! I am going to try to be nice to him but I know I won't! He is so young and so serious that I can't resist shocking him. He does n't approve of giddy young widows that don't look sorry! Neither

do I. In two days I return to the fold.
Until then "My Bonnie" beware!

HIROSHIMA, February 19th, 1902.

After a sleepless night I got up this
morning with a splitting headache. I
have been back in the traces for a
month, and I am beginning to feel like
a poor old horse in a tread mill, not
that I don't love the work, but oh!
Mate, I am so lonesome, lonesome, lonesome. I think I used up so much sand
when I first came that the supply is
running low.

"All day there is the watchful world to face
The sound of tears and laughter fill the air.
For memory there is but scanty space
Nor time for any transport of despair.
But, Love, the pulse beats slow, the lips
turn white
Sometimes at night !"

Perhaps when I am old and gray

and wrinkled I 'll be at peace. But think of the years in between! I have been cheated of the best that life holds for a woman, the love of a good husband, the love of her children, and the joys of a home.

The old world shakes its finger and says "you did it yourself". But, Mate, I was only eighteen, and I did n't know the real from the false. I staked my all for the prize of love, and I lost. Heaven knows I 've paid the penalty, but I 'd do it over again if I thought I was right. The difference is that then I was a child and knew too little, and now I am a woman and know too much.

Sometimes the hymn-singing and praying, and "Sistering" and "Brothering" get on my nerves, until I almost scream, but when I remember how heavenly good to me they are I 'm all contrition. I have even been invited to write for the Mission papers, now is n't that sufficient glory for any sinner?

Your letters are such comforts to me! I read them over and over and actually know parts of them by heart! Since I was a little girl I have had a burning desire to win your approval. I remember once when you said I was stronger than the little boy next door I sprained my back trying to prove it. And now when you write those lovely things about me and tell me how good and brave I am, why I 'd sprain something worse than my back to be worthy of your approval!

But my courage does n't always ring true, Mate, sometimes it 's a brass ring. If you want to hear of true heroism, just listen to this story. There was a little American Missionary, who was going home to stay after twenty years of hard service. At the request of the board she stopped off at the Leper Colony in order to make a report. Soon after she reached home, she discovered a small white spot on her hand, and on consulting a physician, found it was leprosy. Without breathing a word of it to anyone, she bade her family and friends a cheerful good-bye, and came straight back to that Leper Colony, where she took up her work among the outcasts. Never an outcry, never a groan, not even a plea for sympathy! Now how is that for a soldier lady?

It is quite cold to-day and I am indulging in the luxury of a roaring fire. You know the natives use little stoves that they carry around with them, and call "hibachi." But cold as it is, the yard is full of roses and the tea-plants are gorgeous. I don't wonder that the climate gets mixed, out here. Everything else is hind part before.

What do you suppose I 've been longing for all day? A good saddle horse? I feel that a brisk canter would set me straight in a short time. But the only horse in Hiroshima is a mule. A knock-kneed, cross-eyed old mule that bitterly resents the insult of being hitched to something that is a cross between a wheelbarrow and a baby buggy. The driver stands up for the excellent reason that he has no place to sit down! We tried this coupé once for the fun and experience. We got the experience all right but I am not so sure about the fun. We jolted along through the narrow streets scraping first against one house, then against another, while our footman, oh yes we had a footman, ran beside the thoroughbred to help him up when he stumbled.

To-morrow we are to have company. A Salvation Army lassie comes down from Tokio with a brass band. It is the second time in the history of the town that the people have had a chance to hear a brass band, and they are greatly thrilled. I must say I am a bit excited myself; Miss Lessing says she is going to keep me in sight, for fear I will follow the drum away. She need n't worry. I am through following anything in this world but my own nose.

HIROSHIMA, March 25, 1902.

I am absolutely walking on air to-day! Just when I thought my cherished dream of a free kindergarten

72

would have to be given up, the checks
from home came! You were a trump
to get them all interested, and it was
beautiful the way they responded.
Only *why* did you tell Jack? He ought
n't to have sent so much. I 'd send it
back if I were n't afraid of hurting
him.

My head is simply spinning with
plans! We are going to open the school
right away and there are hundreds of
things to be done. In spite of my homesickness, and loneliness and longing for
you loved ones, I would n't come home
now if I could! It is the feeling that I
am needed here, that a big work will
go undone, if I don't do it, that simply
puts my little wants and desires right
out of the question!

Yesterday we had a mothers' meeting, and I have not stopped laughing
over it yet! It seems that the mothers

considered it proper to show their appreciation by absolute solemnity. After tea and cake were served they sat in funeral silence. Not a word nor a smile could we get out of them. When I could n't stand it another minute, I told Miss Lessing I was going to break the ice if I went under in the effort. By means of an interpreter, I told the mothers that we were going to try an American amusement and would they lend their honorable assistance? Then I called in thirty of the school girls and told each one to ask a mother to skip. They were too polite to decline, so to the tune of "Mr. Johnson, Turn Me Loose," the procession started. Miss Dixon could n't stay in the room for laughing. The old and the young, and the fat and the thin caught the spirit of it and went hopping and jumping around the circle in great glee. Af-

ter that, old ladies and all played
"Pussy Wants a Corner," and "Drop
the Handkerchief," and they laughed
and chattered like a lot of children.
They stayed four hours, and we are still
picking up hair ornaments!

Up over my table I have the little
picture you sent of the "Lane that
turned at last". You always said my
lane would turn, and it *has* turned into
a broad road bordered by cherry-blos-
soms and wisteria. But, Mate, you
need n't think there are no more mud-
holes, for there are. When I see them
ahead, I climb the fence and walk
around!

I am getting quite thrilled these days
over the prospect of war. The soldiers
are drilling by the hundreds, and the
bugles are blowing all day. It makes
little thrills run up and down my back,
but Miss Lessing says nothing will

come of it, that Japan is always getting ready for a scrap. But the Trans-Siberian Railway has refused all freight because it is too busy bringing soldiers and supplies to Vladivostock.

Now speaking of Vladivostock reminds me of a plan that has been suggested for next summer. Miss Dixon, the teacher who was sick, is going to Russia and is crazy for me to go with her. It would n't be much more expensive than staying in Japan, and would be tremendously interesting. Don't mention it to anybody at home, but write me if you approve.

I wish you could have peeped into my room last night. Four or five of the girls slipped in after the silence bell had rung, and we sat around the fire on the floor and drank tea while I showed them my photographs. They made such a pretty picture, with their gay gowns and red cheeks, and they were so thrilled over all my things. The pictures from home interested them most of all, especially the one of you and Jack which I have framed together. At first they thought you must be married, and when I said no, they decided that you were lovers, so I let it go.

After they went to bed, I sat and looked at the two pictures in the double frame and wondered how it was after all that you and Jack *had n't* fallen in love with each other! You both live with your heads in the clouds; I should think you would have bumped into each other long before this. He told me once that you had fewer faults than any woman he had ever known. Telling me of other people's virtues was one of Jack's long suits.

My last minute of grace is gone, so

The Lady of the Decoration

I must say good-night. I am getting
up at five o'clock these mornings in
order to get in all that I want to do.

HIROSHIMA, May 31, 1902.

Under promise that I will not write
a long letter, I am allowed to begin
one to you this morning. Miss Lessing
wrote you last week that I had been
sick. The truth is I tried to do too
much, and paid up for it by staying in
bed two whole weeks. Perhaps I will
acquire a little sense in the next world;
I certainly have n't in this! Japan
was n't made for restless, energetic
people. If you can't learn to be lazy,
you can't last long.

I can never tell you how good Miss
Lessing has been, sleeping right by me,
taking care of me and loving me like

78

The Lady of the Decoration

I was her own child. The girls too, have been so good sending me gifts almost every hour in the day. One little girl got up at prayers the other night, and, folding her hands, said: "Oh Lord, please make the Skipping Sensei well, and help me to keep my mouth shut so it will be quiet, for she has been good to us and we all do love her much." Heaven knows the "Skipping Sensei" needs all the prayers of the congregation!

Just as soon as school is over, Miss Dixon and I start for Russia. It's a good thing that vacation is near for I am tired of being a Missionary lady, and a school-marm, in fact I am tired of being good.

Don't worry about me, for I am all right. I 've just run down and need a little fun to wind me up for another year.

The Lady of the Decoration

Does July 16th mean anything to you?
It does to me. Just one year ago to-
day the gates of that old Union Depot
shut between me and all that was dear
to me, and I went out into the big
world to fight my big fight alone. Well,
I am still fighting, Mate, and probably
will be to the end of the campaign.

As you see I am in Kobe waiting for
my pass-port to go to Russia. If there
is anything you want to know about
pass-ports just apply to me. With all
confidence, I sailed down to the Con-
sulate and was met by a pair of legs
attached to a huge mustache and the
funniest little button of a head you ever
saw. I think the Lord must have
laughed when he got through making
that man! He was horribly bored with
life in general, and me in particular.

The Lady of the Decoration

He motioned me wearily to a chair beside a table, and, handing me a paper, managed to sigh: "Fill in."

The questions were about like this: Who was your father? What are you doing out of your own country? Was anybody in your family ever hung? How many teeth have you?

I wrote rapidly until I got to "When were you born?" Button-Head was standing by me, so I looked up at him helplessly and told him that was one thing I *never* could remember. He said I would have to, and I said I could n't. He pranced around for fifteen minutes, and I pretended to be racking my brain.

Then he handed me a Bible, and said in a stern voice: "Swear." I told him that I could n't, that I never had sworn, that ladies did n't do it in America, would n't he please do it for me?

About this time Miss Dixon spoiled

the fun by laughing, so I had to behave.
After we had spent two hours and
three dollars in that dingy old office,
we departed, but our troubles were not
over. No sooner had we reached the
hotel than Button-Head appeared with
more papers. "You failed to describe
yourself," he mournfully announced,
handing me another slip.

I had not had my dinner and I was
cross, but I seized a pen determined
to make short work of it. How tall?
Easily told. Black or white? Very
easy. Kind of chin? Round and rosy.
Shape of face? Depends on time and
place. Hair? Pure gold. Eyes?
Now I knew they were green but that
did not sound poetic enough so I ap-
pealed to Dixie. She thought for a
while, then said, "Not gray nor brown,
I have it, they are syrup colored!" So
I put it down along with a lot of other
nonsense.

The Lady of the Decoration

Now the papers have to be sent to Tokyo for approval, then back here again where I will have to do some more signing and swearing. Is n't this enough to discourage people from ever going anywhere?

The news about the sailboat is great. How many of you will be up at the Cape this summer? Is Jack going? When I think of the starlight nights out in the boat, and the long lazy mornings on the beach, I get absolutely faint with longing. Heretofore I have n't *dared* to enjoy things, and now, when I might, I am an exile heading for Siberia! Oh, well! perhaps there will be starlight nights in Siberia, who knows?

VLADIVOSTOCK, SIBERIA,
August 16, 1902.

If I should write all I wanted to say this morning, my letter would reach

across the Pacific! I did n't believe
it was possible for me ever to have such
a good time again.

When we came, we brought a letter
of introduction to a Mrs. Heath. She
has a beautiful big house, and a beautiful big heart, and she took us right
into both.

The day after we arrived, I was standing on her piazza looking down the bay,
when I saw a battle-ship come sailing in under a salute of seventeen guns
from the fort. It turned out to be the
"Victor," and you never knew such
rejoicing. Mrs. Heath knows all the
navy people and her house is a favorite rendezvous. Before night, we had
met many old acquaintances, among
them my Nagasaki friend, "Vermont."

It has been tremendously jolly and
I can't deny that I have been outrage-
ously frivolous for a missionary! But

84

to save my life I can't conjure up the ghost of a regret! And what is more, I have been contaminating Dixie! I have kept her in such a giddy whirl that she says I have paralysed her conscience! I have dressed her up and trotted her along to lunches, teas and dinners, to concerts on sea and land, and once, Oh! awful confession, I bulldozed her into going to the theatre! The consequence is that she has gotten entirely well and looks ten years younger. Her chief trouble was that she had surrounded herself with a regular picket fence of creed and dogma, and was afraid to lift her eyes for fear she would catch a glimpse through the cracks, of the beautiful world which God meant for us to enjoy. It gave me particular joy to pull a few palings off that picket fence!

Most of my time is spent on the water with Vermont. I don't find it half bad out on the bewitching Uzzuri Bay when the moon is shining and the music floats over the water, to discuss love with a fascinating youth!

What does it matter if he is talking about "the other one"? Don't you suppose that I am glad to know that somewhere in this wide world there's a man that can be loyal to his sweetheart even though she is ten thousand miles away?

I ask occasional questions and don't listen to the answers, and he pours out his confessions and thinks I am lovely. He really is one of the dearest fellows I ever met, and I am glad for that other girl with all my heart.

I like several of the other men very much but they bother me with questions. They refuse to believe that I am connected with a mission, and consider it all as a huge joke.

The Lady of the Decoration

I wish you could see this place. It is built in terraces up the greenest of mountains and forms a crescent around the bay. Everybody seems to be in uniform of some kind, and soldiers and sailors are at every turn. The streets are a glittering panorama of strange color and form. At night everything is ablaze, bands playing, uniforms glittering, and flags flying. It is all just one intense thrill of life and rhythm, and the cloven foot of my worldliness never fails to keep time.

But when daylight comes and all the sordid ugliness is revealed, disgust takes the place of fascination. The streets are crowded with thousands of degraded Chinese and Koreans, who, even in their brutality, are not as bad as the ordinary Russians.

Through this mass of poverty and degradation dash handsome carriages filled with richly clad people. The drivers wear long blue plush blouses with red sleeves and belt, and trousers tucked in high boots. On their heads they wear funny little hats that look as if they had been sat on. They generally stand up while driving and lash the poor horses into a dead run from start to finish. Many of them are ex-convicts and can never leave Siberia. If their cruelty to horses is any criterion of their cruelty to their fellow men, I can't help thinking they deserve their punishment.

I won't dare to mail this letter until I get out of Russia for they are so cranky about their blessed old country. They would not even let me have a little flag to send to the boys at home! I found out to-day that a policeman comes every day to see what we have been doing, what hours we keep, etc. In fact every movement is watched, and one day when we returned to the hotel, we found that all our possessions had been searched, and the police had even left their old cigar stumps among our things! The more you see of Russia, the more deeply you fall in love with Uncle Sam!

Several days ago Mrs. Heath gave us a tennis-tea and we had a jolly time. The tea was served under the trees from a steaming samovar, around which gathered representatives of many nations. There were many unpronounceable gentlemen, and one real English Lord, who considered Americans, "frightfully amusing."

I thought I had forgotten how to play tennis but I had n't. That undercut that Jack taught us won me a reputation.

It is only when I stop to think, that I realize how far I am from home!

The Lady of the Decoration

When I wonder where you all are this minute, and what you are doing, I feel as if I were on a visit to the planet Mars, and had no communication whatever with the world.

Think of me, Mate, in Siberia, eating fish with a spoon, and drinking coffee from a glass! Verily, when old Sister Fate found she could not down me, she must have decided to play pranks with me!

My box of new clothes arrived just before I started, and I have had use for everything. When I get on the white coat suit and the white hat, I feel like a dream.

The weather is simply glorious, like our best October days at home. Nothing could be more unlike than Russia and Japan! one is a great oil painting, tragic, majestic, grand, while the other

The Lady of the Decoration

is an exquisitely dainty water color full
of sunshine and flowers.

Callers have come so I must close.
Life is a very pretty game after all,
especially when you get wise enough
to look on.

VLADIVOSTOCK, SIBERIA,
September 1, 1902.

Just a short letter to tell you that
we leave Vladivostock to-night. I am
all broken up; it has been the happiest
summer that I have had for years and
I can't bear to think of it being over.

It has been so long since Peace and
I have been acquainted that I hardly
yet dare look her full in the face for
fear she will take flight and leave me
in utter darkness again. Even if she
has not come to live with me, she is at

least my next door neighbor, and I offer her incense that she may abide.

Now I might as well confess that if it were not for Memory there is no telling what Peace might do! Poor old Memory! I'd like to throttle her sometime and bury her in a deep hole. Yet she has served me many a good turn, and often laid a restraining hand on impulse and thought. But she is like a poor relation, always turning up at the wrong time!

For instance, on a gorgeous moonlight night on the Uzzuri Bay when you are out in a sampan with a pigtail who neither sees nor hears, and your companion is clever enough to be fascinating and daring enough to say things he "had n't oughter," and the music and the moonlight gets into your head, and you feel young and reckless and sentimental, then all of a sudden

The Lady of the Decoration

Memory recalls another moonlight night when the youth and the romance were n't merely make believe, and your mind travels wearily over the intervening years, and you sit up straight and look severe and put your hands behind you!

Oh! I am clinging to my ideal, Mate, never fear. I 've held on to her garments until they are tattered and torn. You introduced me to her and I have never lost sight of her entirely.

This afternoon the Victor sailed for the Philippines. As she passed Mrs. Heath's cottage where we had all promised to be, she dipped her colors. I felt pretty blue for I knew my good times were on board, and were sailing out of sight.

I am now at the hotel, trunk and boxes packed, waiting to start. Cinderella is not going to wait for the

stroke of twelve; she has donned her
sober garments and is ready to be
whisked back to the cinders on the
hearth. I am glad hard work is ahead;
a solid grind seems necessary for my
soul's salvation.

Farewell, vain earth! I love you
not wisely but too well.

Why can't people be nice to one without being too nice? And why can't you
be horrid to people without being too
horrid? Selah.

HIROSHIMA, October 10, 1902.

Dear Old Mate:

I am so dead tired to-night that I
could not tell what part of me ached
the most! But the spirit moves me to
unburden my soul and I feel that I
must write you. For this is one of my
dream nights, and I have so many in

The Lady of the Decoration

Japan, when my old shell is too exhausted to move, and so permits my soul to wander where it will, a dream night, when the moon is its silveriest and biggest and I want to hug it for I know that twelve hours before it looked down on my loved ones, and now it comes to make more beautiful this fairy land, hiding the scars and ugly places, touching the pine trees with silver points, and glorifying the old Temples, till one wonders if they *could* have been made by hands. A night when the white robed priests are doing honor to some "heathen idol" and must needs call his wandering attention by the stroke of the deep toned bell, which sends its music far across sleeping Japan, out into the wonderful sea.

I don't know what comes over me such nights as these. I don't seem to

95

be me at all! I can lie most of the
night, wide awake, yet unconscious of
my surroundings, and dream dreams.
I live through all the joyful days of
childhood, then through the sorrowful
days of womanhood when I was learning how to live, through the years
of heartache and heart-break,—and
through it all, though I actually suffer,
there is such an unspeakable lightness
and buoyancy, such a lifting up, that
even pain is a pleasure. I can't explain
it all, unless it is the influence of this
mysterious country, lulling and sooth-
ing, but powerful and subtle as poison.

My dear girl you say you feel too
far away to help me! Now don't you
worry about that! If you never wrote
me another line, you would help me.
Just to know that you are around there,
on the other side of the earth, believing
in me, loving me, and *approving* of me,

means everything. You were right to make me come, and while it cost me my very heart's blood, yet I am learning my lesson as you said I would.

My little ship may never again sail into the harbor of happiness, yet there are sunny seas where soft winds blow, and even if my ship is all by its lonesome, yet it 's such a frisky craft, warranted never to sink, no matter what the weather, that it can sail over many seas, touch many lands, and grow rich in experience. And hid away in the locker where no eye save mine may see, are my treasures; your love is one, and nothing can rob me of it.

What you write me of Jack makes me very unhappy. I am not worth his worrying over. Tell him so, Mate. If I could ever care for anybody again in this world, it would be for him, but if an occasional sentiment dares to spring

7

97

up into my heart, I pull it up by the roots! I would give anything to write to him, but I know it would only bring pain to us both. Be good to him, Mate, I can't bear to think of him being miserable.

I am so tired that I can scarcely keep the tears back. I must write no more.

HIROSHIMA, November 14, 1902.

I have about fifteen minutes between classes, and I am going to spend them on you. Now who do you suppose has come to the surface again? Little Germany, who was on the steamer coming over. He wasted a great many stamps on me for the first few months after we landed but he got tired of playing solos. He was on his way to Thibet to enter a monastery to study some ancient language. Heaven knows why he wants to know anything more antique than the language he speaks! I don't believe there is any old dusty, forgotten corner of the world that he has n't poked into.

Well you know the fatal magnetism I exert over fossils! They always turn to me as naturally as needles turn to a loadstone. This particular mummy was no exception.

I wrote him a formal stately answer, reminding him in gentle reproof that I was a widow (God save the Mark) and that my life was dedicated to my work. It was no use, he bombarded me with letters, with bigger and bigger words and longer and fiercer quotations. In the last one he threatens to come to Hiroshima!

If he does, I am going to shave my eye-brows and black my teeth! He speaks seven languages, and yet he does n't know the meaning of the one word "no."

Jack used to say that if a man was persistent enough he could win a woman in spite of the Devil. I would like to see him! I mean Jack, not Dutchy nor the Devil.

HIROSHIMA, Christmas Eve, 1902.

I am in the very thickest of Christmas, and yet such a funny, unreal Christmas, that it does not seem natural at all. Hiroshima is busy decorating for the New Year, and everything is gay with brilliant lanterns, plum blossoms and crimson berries. The little insignificant streets are changed into bowers of sweet smelling ferns and spicy pines, and the bamboo leaves sway to every breeze, while the waxen plum blossoms send out a perfume sweet as violets.

The shop-keepers and their families put on their gayest kimonas and their most enticing smiles and greet you with effusion.

On entering a shop you are asked if your honorable eyes will deign to look upon most unworthy goods. Please will you give this or that a little adoring look? The price? Ah! it's price is greatly enhanced since the august foreigner cast honorable eyes upon it. (Which is no joke!) Whether the article is bought or not, the smile, the bow, the compliment are the same. All this time the crowd around the door of the shop has been steadily increasing until daylight is shut out, for everyone is interested in your purchase from the man who hauls the dray up to the highest lady in the land. The shop-

keeper is very patient with the crowd
until it shuts out the light, then he in-
vites them to carry their useless bodies
to the river and throw them in.

Once outside you see another crowd
and as curiosity is in the air, you crane
your neck and try to get closer. The
center of attraction is a man in spot-
less white cooking bean cake on a little
hibachi. The air is cold and crisp, and
the smell of the savory bean paste,
piping hot, makes you hungry.

Next comes the fish man with a big
flat basket on each end of a pole, and
offers you a choice lot; long slippery
eels, beautiful shrimp, as pink as the
sunset, and juicy oysters whose shells
have been scrubbed until they are
gleaming white. Around the baskets
are garlands of paper roses to hide
from view the ugly rough edges of the
straw.

The Lady of the Decoration

The candy shops tempt you to the last sen, and the toy shops are a perfect joy. Funny fat Japanese dolls and stuffed rabbits and cross-eyed, tailless cats demand attention. Perhaps you will see a cheap American doll with blue eyes and yellow hair carefully exhibited under a glass case, and when you are wondering why they treasure this cheap toy, you happen to glance down and catch the worshipping gaze of a wistful, half starved child, and your point of view changes at once and you begin to understand the value of it, and to wish with all your heart that you could put an American dolly in the hands of every little Japanese girl on the Island!

It is getting almost time to open my box and I am right childish over it. It has been here for two days, and I have slipped in a dozen times to look at it

and touch it. Oh! Mate, the time has
been *so* long, so cruelly long! I wake
myself up in the night some time sob-
bing. One year and a half behind me,
and two and a half ahead! I remember
mother telling about the day I started
to school, how I came home and said
triumphantly, "Just think I 've only
got ten more years to go to school!"

Poor little duffer! She 's still going
to school!

Last night I had another mother's
meeting for the mothers of the Free
Kindergarten. This time I gave a
magic lantern show, and I was the
showman. The poor, ignorant women
sat there bewildered. They had never
seen a piano, and many of them had
never been close to a foreigner before.
I showed them about a hundred slides,
explained through an interpreter until
I was hoarse, gesticulated and orated

104

to no purpose. They remained silent and stolid. By and by there was a stir, heads were raised, and necks craned. A sudden interest swept over the room. I followed their gaze and saw on the sheet the picture of Christ toiling up the mountain under the burden of the cross. The story was new and strange to them, but the fact was as old as life itself. At last they had found something that touched their own lives and brought the quick tears of sympathy to their eyes.

I am going to have a meeting every month for them, no matter what else has to go undone.

It is almost time to hang up our stockings. Miss Lessing and Dixie objected at first, but I told them I was either going to be very foolish or very blue, they could take their choice. I have to do something to scare away the ghosts of dead Christmases, so I put on my fool's cap and jingle my bells. When I begin to weaken, I go to the piano and play "Come Ye Disconsolate" to rag time, and it cheers me up wonderfully.

I guess it's just about daylight with you now. Pete is tiptoeing in to make the fires. I can hear him now saying: "Christmas Gif' Mister Sam, Chris'mus Gif' Miss Bettie!" and the children are flying around in their night clothes wild with excitement. Down in the sitting room the stockings make a circle around the room and underneath each is a pile of gifts. I can see the big log fire, and the sparkle of it in the old book-case, and in the long glass between the windows. And in a few minutes here you all come, you uncles and you cousins and you aunts, trooping in with the smallest first. And such laughing, and shouting, and rejoicing! and maybe in the midst of the fun somebody speaks of me, and there's a little hush, and a little longing, then the fun goes on more furiously than ever.

Well even if I am on the wrong side of the earth in body, I am not in spirit, and I reach my arms clear around the world and cry "God bless you, every one."

HIROSHIMA, March, 1903.

I have a strong conviction that I am going to swear before I get through this letter, for this pen is what I would call, to use unmissionary language, devilish. My! how familiar and wicked that word looks! I've heard so many hymns and so much brotherly and sisterly talk that it seems like meeting an old friend to see it written!

Here it is nearly cherry-blossom

107

time again, and the days and the weeks are slipping away into months before I know it. I am working at full speed and wonder sometimes how I keep up. But I don't dare leave any leisure for heartaches, even when the body is quivering from weariness, and every nerve cries out for rest. I must keep on and on and on, for all too easily the dread memories come creeping back and enfold me until there is no light on any side. From morning until night it is a fight against the tide.

Work is the only thing that keeps me from thinking, and I am determined not to think. I suppose I am as contented here as I could be anywhere. My whole heart is in the kindergarten and the success of it, and maybe the day will come when my work will be all sufficient to satisfy my soul's craving. But it has n't come yet!

The Lady of the Decoration

I almost envy some of these good people who can stand in the middle of one of their prayers and touch all four sides. They know what they want and are satisfied when they get it, but I want the moon and the stars and the sun thrown in.

When things seem closing in upon me and everything looks dark, I flee to the woods. I never knew what the trees and the wind and the sky really meant until I came out here and had to make friends of them. I think you have to be by yourself and a bit lonesome before Nature ever begins to whisper her secrets. Can you imagine Philistine Me going out on the hill top to see the sun-rise and going without my supper to see it set? I am even studying the little botany that Jack gave me, though my time and my intellect are equally limited.

The Lady of the Decoration

And speaking of Jack leads me to remark that there is no necessity for all of you to maintain such an oppressive silence concerning him! Three months ago you wrote me that he was not well, and that he was going south with you and sister. He must be pretty sick to stop work even for a week. I have pictured you sitting with a loaf of bread and a jug of wine beneath the bough quoting poetry at each other to your heart's content.

You say when I come home I can rest on my laurels; no thank you, I want a Morris chair, a pitcher of lemonade, all the new books and a little darkey to fan me.

Mrs. Heath has asked me to visit her in Vladivostock this summer and I am going if the cholera does n't get worse. We are so afraid of it that we almost boil the cow before we drink the milk!

The Lady of the Decoration

Among the delicacies of our menu out here are raw fish, pickled parsnips, sea-weed and bean-paste. As old Charity used to say I 've gotten so "acclamitized" I think I could eat a gum shoe.

When they send out my spring box from home, please tell them to put in some fluffy white dresses with elbow sleeves. Then I want lots of pretty ribbons, and a white belt. I saw in the paper that crushed leather was the proper thing. It sounds like something good to eat, but if it 's to wear send it along.

My disposition will be everlastingly ruined if I write another line with this pen. Good-bye.

The Lady of the Decoration

Well the catastrophe arrived and we were prisoners for nearly a week. It was not quite cholera but close enough to it to scare us all to death. Both Eve and the apple were young and green, and the combination worked disaster. When the doctor arrived, he shipped Eve off to the inspection hospital, while we were locked up, guarded by five small policemen, and hardly allowed to open our mouths for fear we would swallow a germ. We were fumigated and par-boiled until we felt like steam puddings. Nobody was allowed to go in or out, our vegetables were handed to us in a basket on a bamboo pole over the wall. We tied notes to bricks and flung them to our neighbors on the outside. Thank Heaven, the servants were locked in too. Every day a little man with lots of brass buttons and a big voice came and asked anxiously after our honorable insides.

I used every inducement to get them to let me go out for exercise. I fixed a tray with my prettiest cups and sent a pot of steaming coffee and a plate of cake out to the lodge house. Word came back, "We are not permitted to drink or taste food in an infected house." Then I tried them on button-hole bouquets, and when that failed, I got desperate, and announced that I was subject to fits, unless I got regular outside exercise every day. That fetched them and they gave the foreign teachers permission to walk in the country for half an hour provided we did not speak to any one.

Eve was up and having a good time before the school gates were opened.

The Lady of the Decoration

While a prisoner, I did all sorts of odd jobs, patched, mended, darned, wrote letters, and chopped down two trees. The latter was a little out of my line, but the trees were eaten up with caterpillars, and as I could not get anybody to cut them down, I sallied forth and did it myself. My chef stood by and admired the job, but he would not assist for fear he would unwittingly murder one of his ancestors!

You would certainly laugh to see me keeping house with a cook book, a grocery book and a dictionary. The other day I gave directions for poached eggs, and the maid served them in a huge pan full of water.

There are one hundred and twenty-five yellow kids waiting for me so I must hurry away.

The Lady of the Decoration

Vladivostock, Siberia, July, 1903.

I did n't mean that it should be so long a time before I wrote you, but the closing of school, the Commencement, and the getting ready to come up here about finished me. You remember the old darkey song, "Wisht I was in Heaben, settin' down"? Well that was my one ambition and I about realized it when I got up here to Mrs. Heath's and she put me in a hammock in a quiet corner of the porch and made me keep blissfully still for two whole days.

The air is just as bracing, the hills are just as green, and the lights and shadows dance over the harbor just as of old. We have tennis, golf, picnics, sails, and constant jollification, but I don't seem to enjoy it all as I did last summer. It is n't altogether homesickness, though that is chronic, it is a constant longing for I don't know what.

Viewed impersonally, the world is a rattling good show, but instead of smiling at it from the front row in the dress circle, I get to be one of the performers every time.

We have been greatly interested in watching the Russians build a fort on one of their islands near here. They insist there will be no war and at the same time they are mining the harbor and building forts day and night. The minute it is dark the searchlights are kept busy sweeping the harbor in search of something not strictly Russian. I hope I will get back as safely as I got here.

Did I tell you that I stopped over two days in Korea? I had often heard of the Jumping Off Place, but I never expected to actually see it! The people live in the most awful little mud houses, and their poverty is appalling. No streets, no roads, no anything save a fog of melancholy that seems to envelop everything. The terrible helplessness of the people, their ignorance, and isolation are terrible.

The box from home was more than satisfactory. I have thoroughly enjoyed wearing all the pretty things. The hat sister sent was about the size of a turn-table; a strong hat pin and a slight breeze will be all I need to travel to No Man's Land. Sister says it's *moderate*, save the mark! but it really is becoming and when I get it on, my face looks like a pink moon emerging from a fleecy black cloud. I had to practice wearing it in private until I learned to balance it properly.

I shall stay up here through July and then I am thinking of going to

Shanghai with Mrs. Heath's sister, who lives there. I am very fond of her, and I know I would have a good time. I feel a little like a subscription list, being passed around this way, but I simply *have* to keep going every minute when I am not at work.

They are calling up to me from the tennis court so I must stop for the present.

SHANGHAI, CHINA, August, 1903.

The mail goes out this morning and I am determined to get this letter written if I break up a dozen parties. As you see, I am in Shanghai, this wonderful big understudy for Chicago, which seems about as incongruous in its surroundings as a silk hat on a haystack! There are beautiful boulevards, immense houses, splendid public gardens, all hedged in by a yellow mass of orientals.

Every nationality is represented here, and people meet, mingle, and separate in an ever changing throng. At every corner stands a tall majestic Sheik, with head bound in yards of crimson cloth, directing the movements of the crowd. Down the street comes a regiment of English soldiers, so big and determined that one well understands their victories. The ubiquitous Russian makes himself known at every turn, silent and grave, but in his simplest dealings as merciless and greedy as the country he represents. Frenchmen and Germans, and best of all, the unquenchable American, join in the panorama, and the result is something that one does not see anywhere else on the globe. I guess if my dear brethren knew of the theatre parties, dinners and dances I was going to, they would think I was on a toboggan slide for the lower regions! I am not though. I am simply getting a good swing to the pendulum so that I can go back to "the field," and the baby organs and the hymn-singing with better grace. It is very funny, but do you know that for a *steady diet* I can stand the saints much better than I can the sinners!

My friends the Carters live right on the Bund facing the water. They keep lots of horses and many servants, and live in a luxury that only the East can offer. Every morning before I am up a slippery Chinese, all done up in livery, comes to my room and solemnly announces: "Missy bath allee ready, nice morning, good-bye." From that time on I am scarcely allowed to carry my pocket handkerchief!

The Lady of the Decoration

The roads about here are perfect, and we drive for hours past big country houses, all built in English fashion. There is one grewsome feature in the landscape, however, and that is the Chinese graves. In the fields, in the back and front yards, on the highways, any bare space that is large enough to set a box and cover it with a little earth, serves as a burying ground.

I am interested in it all, and enjoying it in a way, but, Mate, there is no use fibbing to you, there is a restlessness in my heart that sometimes almost drives me crazy. There is nothing under God's sun that can repay a woman for the loss of love and home. It's all right to love humanity, but I was born a specialist. The past is torn out by the roots but the awful emptiness remains. I am not grieving over what has been, but what is n't. That last sentence sounds malarial, I am going right upstairs to take a quinine pill.

SOOCHOW, August, 1903.

Well, Mate, this is the first letter I have really written you from China. Shanghai does n't count. Soochow is the real article. The unspeakable quantity and quality of dirt surpasses anything I have ever imagined. Dirt and babies, there are millions of babies, under your feet, around your heels, every nook and corner full of babies.

From Shanghai to Soochow is only a one night trip, and as I had an invitation to come up for over Sunday, I decided to take advantage of it. You would have to see the boat I came in to appreciate it. They call it a house-boat, but it is built on a pattern that is new to me. In the lower part are rooms, each of which is supplied with a board on which you are supposed to sleep. Each passenger carries his own bedding and food. In the upper part of the boat is a sort of loft just high enough for a man to sit up, and in it are crowded hundreds of the common people. A launch tows seven or eight of these house-boats at a time. I will not ask you to even imagine the condition of them; I had to stand it because I was there, but you are not.

It was just at sunset when we left Shanghai, and I got as far away from the crowd as I could and tried to forget my unsavory surroundings. The sails of thousands of Chinese vessels loomed black and big against the red sky as they floated silently by without a ripple. In the dim light, I read on the prow of a bulky schooner, " 'The

Mary', Boston, U.S.A.'' Do you know
how my heart leapt out to ''The Mary,
Boston, U.S.A.''? It was the one thing
in all that vast, unfamiliar world that
spoke my tongue.

When I went to my room, I found
that a nice little Chinese girl in a long
sack coat and shiny black trousers was
to share it with me. I must confess
that I was relieved for I was lonesome
and a bit nervous, and when I discovered that she knew a little English I
could have hugged her. We spread
our cold supper on the top of my dress
suit case, put our one candle in the center, and proceeded to feast. Little Miss
Izy was not as shy as she looked, and
what she lacked in vocabulary she made
up in enthusiasm. We got into a gale
of laughter over our efforts to understand each other, and she was as curious about my costume as I was about

124

hers. She watched me undress with unfeigned amusement, following the lengthy process carefully, then she rose, untied a string, stepped out of her coat and trousers, stood for a moment in a white suit made exactly like her outer garments, then gaily kicked off her tiny slippers and rolled over in bed. I don't know if this is a universal custom in China, but at any rate, little Miss Izy will never be like the old lady, who committed suicide because she was so tired of buttoning and unbuttoning.

The next morning we were in Soochow, at least outside of the city wall. They say the wall is over two thousand years old and it certainly looks it, and the spaces on top left for the guns to point through make it look as if it had lost most of its teeth. Things are so old in this place, Mate, that I feel as if I had just been born! I have nearly run my legs off sightseeing; big pagodas and little pagodas, Mamma Buddhas and Papa Buddhas, and baby Buddhas, all of whom look exactly like their first cousins in Japan.

Soochow is just a collection of narrow alley-ways over which the house tops meet, and through which the people swarm by the millions, sellers crying their wares, merchants urging patronage, children screaming, beggars displaying their infirmities, and through it all coolies carrying sedan chairs scattering the crowd before them.

In many of the temples, the priests hang wind bells to frighten the evil spirits away. I think it is a needless precaution, for it would only be a feeble-minded spirit that would ever want to return to China once it had gotten away!

The Lady of the Decoration

In harness again and glad of it.
I 've opened the third kindergarten
with the money from home; it 's only
a little one, eighteen children in all, and
there were seventy-five applicants, but
it is a beginning. You ought to see
the mothers crowding around, begging
and pleading for their children to be
taken in, and the little tots weep and
wail when they have to go home. I
feel to-day as if I would almost resort
to highway robbery to get money
enough to carry on this work!

My training class is just as interesting as it can be. When the girls came
to me two years ago they were in the
Third Reader. With two exceptions,
I have given them everything that was
included in my own course at home,

and taught them English besides. They are very ambitious, and what do you suppose is their chief aim in life? To study until they know as much as I do! Oh! Mate, it makes me want to hide my head in shame, when I think of all the opportunities I wasted. You know only too well what a miserable little rubbish pile of learning I possess, but what you *don't* know is how I have studied and toiled and burned the midnight tallow in trying to work over those old odds and ends into something useful for my girls. If they have made such progress under a superficial, shallow-pated thing like me, what *would* they have done under a woman with brains?

I wish you could look in on me to-night sitting here surrounded by all my household goods. The room is bright and cozy, and just at present

The Lady of the Decoration

I have a room-mate. It is a little sick girl from the training class, whom I have taken care of since I came back. She belongs to a very poor family down in the country, her mother is dead, and her home life is very unhappy. She nearly breaks her heart crying when we speak of sending her home, and begs me to help her get well so she can go on with her studies.

Of course she is a great care, but I get up a little earlier and go to bed a little later, and so manage to get it all in.

We are getting quite stirred up over the war clouds that are hanging over this little water-color country. Savage old Russia is doing a lot of bullying, and the Japanese are not going to stand much more. They are drilling and marching and soldiering now for all they are worth. From Kuri, the naval station, we can hear the thunder of the guns which are in constant practice. Out on the parade grounds, in the barracks, on every country road preparation is going on. Officers high in rank and from the Emperor's guard are here reviewing the troops. Those who know say a crash is bound to come. So if you hear of me in a red cross uniform at the front, you need n't be surprised.

HIROSHIMA, November, 1903.

My dear old Mate:

I am just tired enough to-night to fold my hands, and turn up my toes and say "Enough." If overcoming difficulties makes character, then I will have as many characters as the Chinese alphabet by the time I get through. The bothers meet me when the girl makes the fire in the morning and puts the ashes in the grate instead of the coal, and they keep right along with me all day until I go to bed at night and find the sheet under the mattress and the pillows at the foot.

It would n't be near so hard if I could charge around, and let off a little of my wrath, but no, I must be nice and sweet and polite and *never* forget that I am an Example.

Have you ever seen these dolls that have a weight in them, so that you can push them over and they stand right up again? Well I have a large one and her name is Susie Damn. When things reach the limit of endurance, I take it out on Susie Damn. I box her jaws and knock her over, and up she comes every time with such a pleasant smile that I get in a good humor again.

What is the matter with you at home?

The Lady of the Decoration

Why don't you write to me? I used to get ten and twelve letters every mail, and now if I get one I am ready to cry for joy. Because I am busy does not mean that I have n't time to be lonely. Why, Mate, you can never know what loneliness means until you are entirely away from everything you love. I have tried to be brave but I have n't always made a grand success of it. What I have suffered—well don't let me talk about it. As Little Germany says, to live is to love, and to love is to suffer. And yet it is for that love we are ready to suffer and die, and without it life is a blank, a sail without a wind, a frame without the picture!

Now to-morrow I may get one of your big letters, and you will tell me how grand I am, and how my soul is developing, etc., and I 'll get such a stiff upper lip that my front teeth will be in danger. It takes a stiff upper lip, and a stiff conscience, and a stiff everything else to keep going out here!

From the foregoing outburst you probably think I am pale and dejected. "No, on the contrary," as the seasick Frenchman said when asked if he had dined. I am hale and hearty, and I never had as much color in my life. The work is booming, and I have all sorts of things to be thankful for.

Our little household has been very much upset this week by the death of our cook. The funeral took place last night at seven o'clock from the lodge house at the gate. The shadows made on the paper screens as they prepared him for burial, told an uncanny story. The lack of delicacy, the coarseness, the total disregard for the dignity of death were all pictured on the doors.

The Lady of the Decoration

I stood in the chapel and watched with a sick heart. After they had crowded the poor old body into a sitting position in a sort of square tub, they brought it out to the coolies who were to carry it to the temple, and afterward to the crematory. The lanterns flickered with an unsteady light, making grotesque figures that seemed to dance in fiendish glee on the grass. The men laughed and chattered, and at last shouldered their burden and trotted off as merrily as if they were going to a matsuri. I never before felt the cruelty of heathenism so keenly. No punishment in the next world can equal the things they miss in this life by a lack of belief in a personal God.

It must be very beautiful at home about this time. The beech trees are all green and gold, and the maples are blazing. I am thinking too about the shadows on the old ice-house. I know every one of them by heart, and they often come to haunt me as do many other shadows of the sad, sad past.

HIROSHIMA, December, 1903.

God bless you honey, I 've got a holiday and I 've sworn vengeance on anyone who comes to my door until I have written my Christmas letters. I wish I was a doctor and a trained nurse, and a scholar, a magician, a philosopher and a saint all combined. I need them in my business.

I have spent this merry Christmas season, chasing from pillow to post with bandages, hot water bags, poultices and bottles. We have had a regular hospital. All the Christmas money I had saved to buy presents for home went in Cod Liver Oil, and Miss Lessing, bless her soul, is doing without a coat for the same purpose. When you see a girl struggling for what little education she can get, and know what sacrifices are being made for it, you just hate your frumpery old finery, and you want to convert everything you possess into cash to help her. All the teachers are doing without fires in their rooms this winter, and it is rather chillsome to go to bed cold and wake up next morning in the same condition. When I get home to a furnace-heated house and have cream in my coffee, I shall feel too dissipated to be respectable!

We have not been able to get a new cook since our old one died, and the fact must have gotten abroad, for all the floating brethren and sisters in Japan have been to see us! Y.M.C.A.'s, W.C.T.U.'s, A.W.B.M.'s and X.Y.Z.'s

have sifted in, and we have to sit up
and be Marthas and Marys all at the
same time!

Sometimes I want to get my hat and
run and run until I get to another
planet. But I am not made of the stuff
that runs, and I have the satisfaction
of knowing that I have stuck to my
post. If sacrificing self, and knocking
longings in the head, and smashing
heart-aches right and left, do not pass
me through the Golden Gate, then I 'll
sue Peter for damages.

It 's snowing to-day, but the old
Earth is making about as poor a bluff
at being Christmasy as I am. The
leaves are all on the trees, many flowers
are in bloom, and the scarlet geraniums
are warm enough to melt the snow
flakes.

My big box has arrived and I am
keeping it until to-morrow. I go out

and sit on it every little while to keep cheered up. This is my third Christmas from home, one more and then—!

There has been too much sickness to make much of the holiday, but I have rigged up a fish pond for the kindergarten children, and each kiddie will have a present that cost one-fourth of a cent! I wish I had a hundred dollars to spend on them!

To-night when the lights are out, my little sick girl's stocking will hang on one bed post, and mine on the other. I don't believe Santa Claus will have the heart to pass us by, do you?

HIROSHIMA, January, 1904.

Here it is January and I am just thanking you dear ones for my beautiful Christmas box. As you probably guessed, Mate, our Christmas was not exactly hilarious. The winter has been a hard one, the prospect of war has sent the price of provisions out of sight, the sick girls in the school have needed medicine and fires, so altogether Miss Lessing, Miss Dixon and I have had to do considerable tugging at the ends to get them to meet. None of us have bought a stitch of new clothing this winter, so when our boxes came, we were positively dazed by all the grandeur.

They arrived late at night and we got out of bed to open them. The first thing I struck was a very crumpled little paper doll, with baby Bess' name printed in topsy-turvy letters on the back. For the next five minutes I was kept busy swallowing the lumps that came in my throat, but Dixie had some peppermint candy out of her box, the first I had seen since I had left home, so I put on my lovely new beaver hat, which with my low-necked gown and red slippers was particularly chic, and I sat on the floor and ate candy. It— the hat and the candy too, went a long way towards restoring my equanimity, but I did n't dare look at that paper doll again that night!

You ask if I mind wearing that beautiful crêpe de chine which is not becoming to you? Well, Mate, I suppose there was a day when I would have scorned anybody's cast-off clothes, but I pledge you my word a queen in her coronation robes never felt half so grand as I feel in that dress! Somehow I seem to assume some of your personality, I look tall and graceful and dignified, and I try to imagine how it feels to be good and intellectual, and fascinating, and besides I have the satisfaction of knowing that I am rather becoming to the dress myself! It fits without a wrinkle and next summer with my big black hat,——! Well, if Little Germany sees me, there will be something doing!

I must tell you an experience I had the other day. Miss Lessing and I were coming back on the train from Miyajima and sitting opposite to us was an old couple who very soon told us that they had never seen foreigners before. They were as guileless as children, and presently the old man came over and asked if he might look at my jacket. I had no objections, so he put his hands lightly on my shoulders and turned me around for inspection. "But," he said to Miss Lessing in Japanese, "how does she get into it?" I took it off to show him and in so doing revealed fresh wonders. He returned to his wife, and after a long consultation, and many inquiring looks, he came back. He said he knew he was a great trouble, but I was most honorably kind, and would I tell him why I wore a piece of leather about my waist, and would I please remove my dress and show them how I put it on? He was distinctly disappointed when I declined, but he managed to get in one more question and that was if we slept in our hats. When he got off, he assured us that he had never seen anything so interesting in his life, and he would have great things to tell the people of his village.

There is n't a place you go, or a thing you do out here that does n't afford some kind of amusement.

The first glamour of the country has gotten dimmed a bit, not that the interest has waned for a moment, but I have come to see that the beauty and picturesqueness are largely on the surface. If ever I have to distribute tracts in another world, I am going to wrap a piece of soap in every one, for I am more and more convinced that the surest way to heaven for the heathen is the Soapy Way.

During the holidays I tried to study up a little and add a drop or two to that gray matter that is supposed to be floating around in my brain. But as a girl said of a child in Kindergarten, "my intelligence was not working." Putting Psychology into easy terms, stopping to explain things I do not understand very well myself, struggling through the medium of a strange language, and trying to occidentalize the oriental mind has been a stiff proposition for one whose learning was never her long suit! When I come home I may be nothing but a giggly, childishly happy old lady, who does n't care a rap whether her skin fits or not.

The prospect of war is getting more and more serious. Out in the Inland Sea, the war ships are hastening here and there on all sorts of secret missions. I hope with all my heart there will not be war, but if there is, I hope Japan will wipe Russia right off the map!

HIROSHIMA, February, 1904.

Dear old Mate:

I am breathless! For three weeks I have had a chase up hill and down dale, to the top of pine clad mountains, into the misty shadows of the deep valleys, up and down the silvery river, to and fro on the frosty road. For why? All because I had lost my "poise," that treasured possession which you said I was to hang on to

144

as I do to my front teeth and my hair.
So when I found it was gone, I started
in full pursuit. Never a sight of its
coat tails did I catch until Sunday,
when I gave up the race and sat me
down to fight out the old fight of rebellion, and kicking against the pricks.

It was a perfect day, the plum trees
were white with blossom, the spice
bushes heavy with fragrance, the river
dancing for joy, and the whole earth
springing into new, tender life. A
saucy little bird sat on an old stone
lantern, and sang straight at me. He
told me I was a whiney young person,
that it was lots more fun to catch
worms and fly around in the sunshine
than it was to sit in the house and
mope. He actually laughed at me, and
I seized my hat and lit out after him,
and when I came home I found I had
caught my "poise."

To-day in class I asked my girls

what "happiness" meant. One new girl looked up timidly and said, "Sensei, I sink him just mean *you*." I felt like a hypocrite, but it pleased me to know that on the outside at least I kept shiny.

I tell you if I don't find my real self out here, if I don't see my own soul in all its bareness and weakness then I will never see it. At home hedged in by conventionality, custom, and the hundred little interests of our daily life, we have small chance to see ourselves as we really are, but in a foreign land stripped bare of everything in the world save *self*, in a loneliness as great sometimes as the grave, face to face with new conditions, new demands, we have ample chance to take our own measurement. I cannot say that the result obtained is calculated to make one conceited!

The Lady of the Decoration

I fit into this life out here, like a square peg in a round hole. I am not consecrated, I was never "*called* to the foreign field*," I love the world and the flesh even if I don't care especially for the devil, I don't believe the Lord makes the cook steal so I may be more patient, and I don't pray for wisdom in selecting a new pair of shoes. When my position becomes unbearable, I invariably face the matter frankly and remind myself that if it is hard on the peg, it is just as hard on the hole, and that if they can stand it I guess I can!

You ask about my reading. Yes, I read every spare minute I can get, before breakfast, on my way to classes, and after I go to bed. Somebody at home sends me the magazines regularly and I keep them going for months.

By the way I wish you would write and tell me just exactly how Jack is.

The Lady of the Decoration

You said he was working too hard and that he looked all fagged out. Was n't it exactly like him to back out of going South on account of his conscience? He would laugh at us for saying it was that, but it was. He may be unreligious, and scoff at churches and all that, but he has the most rigid, cast-iron, inelastic conscience that I ever came across. I wish he would take a rest. You see out here, so far away from you all, I can't help worrying when any of you are the least bit sick. Jack has been on my mind for days. Don't tell him that I asked you to, but won't you get him to go away? He would curl his hair if you asked him to.

Preparations for war are still in progress and it makes a fellow pretty shivery to see it coming closer and closer. Hiroshima will be the center of military movements and of course un-

der military law. It will affect us only
as to the restrictions put on our walks
and places we can go. With the city
so full of strange soldiers, I don't suppose we will want to go much. Two
big war ships, which Japan has just
bought from Chili are on their way
from Shanghai. Regiment after regiment has poured into Hiroshima and
embarked again for Corea. I am terribly thrilled over it all, and the Japanese watch my enthusiasm with their
non-committal eyes and never say a
word!

My poor little sick girl grows weaker
all the time. She is a constant care
and anxiety, but she has no money
and I cannot send her back to her
wretched home. The teachers think I
am very foolish to let the thing run
on, and I suppose I am. She can never
be any better, and she may live this

149

way for months. But when she clings
to me with her frail hands and declares
she is better and will soon get well if
I will only let her stay with me, my
heart fails me. I have patched up an
old steamer chair for her, and made
a window garden, and tried to make
the room as bright as possible. She
has to stay by herself nearly all day,
but she is so patient and gentle that
I never hear a complaint. This
morning she pressed my hand to her
breast and said wistfully, "Sensei, it
makes sorry to play all the time with
the health."

Miss Lessing tried to get her in the
hospital but they will not take incur-
ables.

Somehow Jack's hospital scheme
does n't seem as foolish as it did. If
there are other children in the world
as friendless and dependent as this

one, then making a permanent home for them would be worth all the great careers in the world.

HIROSHIMA, March, 1904.

My Best Girl:

Don't I wish you were here to share all these thrills with me! War is actually in progress, and if you could see me hanging out of the window at midnight yelling for a special, then chasing madly around to get someone to translate it for me, see me dancing in fiendish glee at every victory won by this brave little country, you would conclude that I am just as young as I used to be. I tell you I could n't be prouder of my own country! Just think of plucky little old Japan winning three battles from those big, brutal, conceited Russians. Why I just want to run and hug the Emperor!

And the school girls! Why their placid faces are positively glorified by the fire of patriotism. Once a week a trained nurse comes to give talks on nursing, and if I go into any corner afterward, I find a group of girls practising all kinds of bandaging. Even the demurest little maiden cherishes the hope that some fate may send her to the battle-field, or that in some way she may be permitted to serve her country.

I am afraid I am not very strict about talking in class these days, but, somehow, courage, nobility, and self-sacrifice seem just as worthy of attention as "motor ideas," and "apperceptions."

A British guest who hates everything Japanese says my enthusiasm "is quite annoying, you know,'' but, dear me, I don't mind him. What could you expect of a person who eats pie with a spoon? Why my enthusiasm is just cutting its eye-teeth! The whole country is a-thrill, and even a wooden Indian would get excited.

Every afternoon we walk down on the sea wall and watch the preparations going on for a long siege. Hundreds of big ships fill the harbor to say nothing of the small ones, and there are thousands of coolies working like mad. I could tell you many interesting things, but I am afraid of the censor. If he deciphers all my letters home, he will probably have nervous prostration by the time the war is over.

Many of the war ships are coaled by women who carry heavy baskets on each end of a pole swung across the shoulder, and invariably a baby on their backs. It is something terrible the way the women work, often pulling loads that would require a horse at home. They go plodding past us on the road, dressed as men, mouth open, eyes straining, all intelligence and interest gone from their faces.

One day as Miss Lessing and I were resting by the roadside, one of these women stopped for breath just in front of us. She was pushing a heavy cart and her poor old body was trembling from the strain. Her legs were bare, and her feet were cut by the stones. There was absolute stolidity in her weather-beaten face, and the hands that lighted her pipe were gnarled and black. Miss Lessing has a perfect genius for getting at people, I think it is her good kind face through which her soul shines. She asked the old woman if she was very tired. The woman looked up, as if seeing us for the first time and nodded her head. Then a queer look came into her face and she asked Miss Lessing if we were the kind of people who had a new God. Miss Lessing told her we were Christians. With a wistfulness that I have never seen except in the eyes of a dog, she said, "If I paid your God with offering and prayers, do you think he would make my work easier? I am so tired!" Miss Lessing made her sit down by her on the grass, and talked to her in Japanese about the new God who did not take any pay for his help, and who could put something in her heart that would give her strength to bear any burden. I could not understand much of what they said but I had a little prayer-meeting all by myself.

HIROSHIMA, April, 1904.

Yesterday the American mail came

after a three weeks' delay. None of us were good for anything the rest of the day. Twenty letters and fifty-two papers for me! Do you wonder that I almost danced a hole in the parlor rug?

The home news was all so bright and cheery, and your letter was such a bunch of comfort that I felt like a two year old. It was exactly like you to think out that little farm party and get Jack into it as a matter of accommodation to you. I followed everything you did, with the keenest interest, from the all-day tramps in the woods, to the cozy evenings around the log fire. I can see old Jack now, at first bored to death but resolved to die if need be on the altar of friendship, gradually warming up as he always does out of doors, and ending up by being the life of the party. He once told me that social success is the infinite capacity for being bored. I know the little outing did him a world of good, and you are all the trumps in the deck as usual.

Who is the Dr. Leet that was in the party? I remember dancing a cotillon with a very good looking youth of that name in the prehistoric ages. He was a senior at Yale, very rich and very good looking. I wore his fraternity pin over my heart for a whole week afterward.

We have been having great fun over the American accounts of the war. Through the newspapers we learn the most marvelous things about Japan and her people. Large cities are unblushingly moved from the coast to an island in the Inland Sea, troops are passported from places which have no harbor, and the people are credited with unheard of customs.

We are still in the midst of stirring

times. The city is overflowing with
troops, and we are hemmed in on every
side by soldiers. Of course foreign
women are very curious to them, and
they often follow us and make funny
comments, but we have never yet had
a single rudeness shown us. In all the
thousands of soldiers stationed here, I
have only seen two who were tipsy, and
they were mildly hilarious from saki.
There is perfect order and discipline,
and after nine o'clock at night the
streets are as quiet as a mountain
village.

The other night, five of the soldiers,
mere boys, donned citizens' dress and
went out for a lark. At roll-call they
were missing and a guard was sent to
search for them. When found, they
resisted arrest and three minutes after
they all answered the roll-call in another world.

And yet although the discipline is

so severe, the men seem a contented and happy lot. They stroll along the roads when off duty hand in hand like school girls, and laugh and chatter as if life were a big holiday. But when the time comes to go to the front, they don their gay little uniforms, and march just as joyfully away to give the last drop of their blood for their Emperor.

I tell you, Mate, I want to get out in the street and cheer every regiment that passes! No drum, no fife, no inspiring music to stir their blood and strengthen their courage, nothing but the unvarying monotony of the four note trumpets. They don't need music to make them go. They are perfect little machines whose motive power is a patriotism so absolute, so complete, that it makes death on the battle-field an honor worthy of deification.

I look out into the play-ground, and

every boy down to the smallest baby
in the kindergarten is armed with a
bamboo gun. Such drilling and marching, and attacking of forts you have
never seen. That the enemy is nothing more than sticks stuck at all
angles matters little. An enemy there
must be, and the worst boy in Japan
would die before he would even *play*
at being a Russian! If Kuropatkin
could see just one of these awful on-
slaughts, he would run up the white
flag and hie himself to safety. So
you see we are well guarded and with
quiet little soldiers on the outside, and
very noisy and fierce little soldiers on
the inside, we fear no invasion of our
peaceful compound.

On my walks around the barracks,
I often pass the cook house, and watch
the food being carried to the mess
room. The rice buckets, about the size

of our water buckets, are put on a pole in groups of six or eight and carried on the shoulders of two men. There is a line about a square long of these buckets, and then another long line follows with trays of soup bowls. Tea is not as a rule drunk with the meals, but after the last grain of rice has been chased from the slippery sides of the bowl, hot water is poured in and sipped with loud appreciation.

Last Sunday afternoon we had to entertain ten officers of high rank, and it proved a regular lark. Their English and our Japanese got fatally twisted. One man took great pride in showing me how much too big his clothes were, giving him ample opportunity to put on several suits of underwear in cold weather; he said "Many cloth dese trusers hab, no fit like 'Merican." They were delighted with all our foreign possessions, and inspected everything minutely. On leaving, one officer bowed low, and assured me that he would never see me on earth again, but he hoped he would see me in heaven *first*!

The breezes from China waft an occasional despairing epistle from Little Germany, but they find me as cold as a snow bank on the north side of a mountain. The sun that melts my heart will have to rise in the west, and get up early at that.

HIROSHIMA, May, 1904.

Well commencement is over and my first class is graduated. Now if you have ever heard of anything more ridiculous than that please cable me! If you could have seen me standing on the platform dealing out diplomas, you would have been highly edified.

The Lady of the Decoration

Last night I gave the class a dinner. There were fourteen girls, only two of whom had ever been at a foreign table before. At first they were terribly embarrassed, but before long they warmed up to the occasion and got terribly tickled over their awkwardness. I was afraid they would knock their teeth out with the knives and forks, and the feat of getting soup from the spoon to the mouth proved so difficult that I let them drink it from the bowl. Sitting in chairs was as hard for them as sitting on the floor for me, so between the courses we had a kind of cake walk.

Next week school begins again, and I start three new kindergartens, making seven over which I have supervision. I am so pleased over the progress of my work that I don't know what to do. Not that I don't realize my limitations, heaven knows I do.

The Lady of the Decoration

Imagine my efforts at teaching the training class psychology! The other day we were struggling with the subject of reflex action, and one of the girls handed in this definition as she had understood it from me! "Reflex action is of a activity nervous. It is sometimes the don't understand of what it is doing and stops many messages to the brain and sends the motion to the legs." What little knowledge I start with gets cross-eyed before I get through.

The Japanese can twist the English language into some of the strangest knots that you ever saw. There is a sign quite near here that reads "Cows milk and Retailed."

Since writing you last, I have sent my little sick girl home. It almost broke us all up, but she could n't stay here alone during the summer and there was nobody to take care of her. I write to her every week and try to keep her cheered up, but for such as she there is only one release and that is death.

If Jack's hospital ever materializes, I am going to offer my services as a nurse. This poor child's plight has taken such a hold upon me that I long to do something for all the sick waifs in creation.

HIROSHIMA, June, 1904.

It is Sunday afternoon, and your Foreign Missionary Kindergarten Teacher, instead of trudging off to Sunday School with the other teachers, is recklessly sitting in dressing gown and slippers with her golden hair hanging down her back, writing letters home. After teaching all week, and listening for two hours to a Japanese sermon Sunday morning, I cross my fingers on teaching Sunday School in the afternoon.

This past week I have been trying to practice the simple life. It was a good time for we had spring cleaning, five guests, daily prayer-meetings, two new cooks, and an earthquake. I think by the time I get through, I'll be qualified to run a government on some small Pacific Isle.

The whole city is in confusion, ninety thousand soldiers are here now, and eighty thousand more are expected this week. Every house-holder must take as many as he can accommodate, and the strain on the people is heavy.

We heard yesterday of the terrible disaster to the troops that left here on the 13th, three transports were sunk by the Russians. Five hundred of the wounded from South Hill battle have been brought here, and whenever I go out, I see long lines of stretchers and covered ambulances bringing in more men. It is intolerable to be near so much suffering and not to be able to relieve it. We are all so worked up with pity and indignation, and sympathy that we hardly dare talk about the war.

Summer vacation will soon be here and I am planning a wild career of self indulgence. I am going to Karuizawa, where I can get cooled off and rested and invite my soul to my heart's content.

For two mortal weeks the rain has poured in torrents. The rainy season out here is n't any of your nice polite little shower-a-day affairs, it is just one interminable downpour, until the old earth is spanked into submission.

167

The Lady of the Decoration

I can't even remember how sunshine looks, and my spirits are mildewed and my courage is mouldy.

To add to the discomfort, we are besieged by mosquitoes. They are the big ferocious kind that carry off a finger at a time. I heard of one missionary down in the country, who was so bothered one night that he hung his trousers to the ceiling, and put his head in one leg, and made his wife put her head in the other, while the rest of the garment served as a breathing tube!

It has been nearly a year since I was out of Hiroshima, a year of such ups and downs that I feel as if I had been digging out my salvation with a pick-ax.

Not that I do not enjoy the struggle; real life with all its knocks and bumps, its joys and sorrows, is vastly preferable to a passive existence of indolence. Only occasionally I look forward to the time when I shall be an angel frivoling in the eternal blue! Just think of being reduced to a nice little curly head and a pair of wings! That's the kind of angel I am going to be. With no legs to ache, and no heart to break— but dear me it is more than likely that I will get rheumatism in my wings!

If ever I do get to heaven, it will be on your ladder, Mate. You have coaxed me up with confidence and praise, you have steadied me with ethical culture books, and essays, and sermons. You have gotten me so far up (for me), that I am afraid to look down. I shrink with a mighty shrivel when I think of disappointing you in any way, and I expand almost to bursting when I think of justifying your belief in me.

The Lady of the Decoration

KARUIZAWA, July, 1904.

Here I am comfortably established in
the most curious sort of double-bar-
reled house you ever saw. The front
part is all Japanese and faces on one
street, and the back part is foreign and
faces on another street a square away.
The two are connected by a covered
walk which passes over a mill race. In
the floor of the walk just over the water is a trap door, and look out when
I will I can see the Japanese stopping
to take a bath in this little opening.

I have a nice big room and so much
service thrown in that it embarrasses
me. When I come in, in the evening,
three little maids escort me to my room,
one fixes the mosquito bar, one gets my
gown, and one helps to undress me.
When they have done all they can

think of, they get in a row, all bow together, then pitter patter away.

The clerk has to make out the menus and as his English is limited, he calls upon me very often to help him. Yesterday he came with only one entry and that was "Corns on the ear." In return for my assistance he always announces my bath, and escorts me to the bath room carrying my sponge and towels.

As to Karuizawa, it has a summer population of about four hundred, three hundred and ninety-nine of whom are missionaries. Let us all unite in singing "Blest be the tie that binds."

Everybody at our table is in the mission field. A long-nosed young preacher who sits opposite me looks as if he had spent all his life in some kind of a field. He has a terrible attack of religion; I never saw anybody take it

any harder. He told me that he was
engaged to be married and for three
days he had been consulting the Lord
about what kind of a ring he should
buy!

Sunday I went to church and heard
my first English sermon in two years.
We met in a rough little shanty, built
in a cluster of pines, and almost every
nation was represented. A young English clergyman read the service, and
afterward said a few words about sacrifice. He was simple and sincere,
and his deep voice trembled with earnestness as he declared that sacrifice
was the only true road to happiness,
sacrifice of ourselves, our wishes and
desires, for the good and the progress
of others. And suddenly all the feeling in me got on a rampage and I
wanted to get up and say that it was
true, that I knew it was true, that the
most miserable, pitiful, smashed-up

life, could blossom again if it would only blossom for others. I walked home in a sort of ecstasy and at dinner the long-nosed young preacher said: "'T was a pity we could n't have regular preaching, there was such a peart lot at meeting." This is certainly a good place to study people's eccentricities, their foibles and follies, to hear them preach and see them *not* practice!

One more year and I will be home. Something almost stops in my heart as I write it! Of course I am glad you are going abroad in the spring, you have been living on the prospect of seeing Italy all your life. Only, Mate, I am selfish enough to want you back by the time I get home. It would take just one perfect hour of seeing you all together once more to banish the loneliness of all these years!

I am glad Jack and Dr. Leet have

struck up such a friendship. Jack uses about the same care in selecting a friend that most men do in selecting a wife. Tell Dr. Leet that I am glad he found me in a pigeon hole of his memory, but that I am a long way from being "the blue-eyed bunch of mischief" he describes. I wish you would tell him that I am slender, pale, and pensive with a glamour of romance and mystery hovering about me; that is the way I would like to be.

I knew you could get Jack out of his rut if you tried. The Browning evenings must be highly diverting, I can imagine you reading a few lines for him to expound, then him reading a few for you to explain, then both gazing into space with "the infinite cry of finite hearts that yearn!"

Dear loyal old Jack! How memories stab me as I think of him. It seems impossible to think of him as other than well and strong and self reliant. What happy, happy days I have spent with him! They seem to stand out to-night in one great white spot of cheerfulness. When the days were the darkest and I could n't see one inch ahead, Jack would happen along with a funny story or a joke, would pretend not to see what was going on, but do some little kindness that would brighten the way a bit. What a mixture he is of tenderness, and brusqueness, of common sense and poetry, of fun and seriousness! I think you and I are the only ones in the world who quite understand his heights and depths. He says even I don't.

KARUIZAWA, July, 1904.

Since writing you I have had the

pleasure of looking six hundred feet down the throat of Asamayama, the great volcano. If the old lady had been impolite enough to stick out her tongue, I would at present be a cinder.

We started at seven in the evening on horseback. Now as you know I have ridden pretty much everything from a broom stick to a camel, but for absolute novelty of motion commend me to a Japanese horse. There is a lurch to larboard, then a lurch to starboard, with a sort of "shiver-my-timbers" interlude. A coolie walks at the head of each horse, and reasons softly with him when he misbehaves. We rode for thirteen miles to the foot of the volcano, then at one o'clock we left the horses with one of the men and began to climb. Each climber·was tied to a coolie whose duty it was to pull, and to carry the lantern. We made a weird procession, and the strange call of the coolies as they bent their bodies to the task, mingled with the laughter and exclamations of the party.

For some miles the pine trees and undergrowth covered the mountain, then came a stretch of utter barrenness and isolation. Miles above yet seemingly close enough to touch rose tongues of flame and crimson smoke. Above was the majestic serenity of the summer night, below the peaceful valley, with the twinkling lights of far away villages. It was a queer sensation to be hanging thus between earth and sky, and to feel that the only thing between me and death was a small Japanese coolie, who was half dragging me up a mountain side that was so straight it was sway-back!

When at last we reached the top, daylight was showing faintly in the east. Slowly and with a glory unspeakable the sun rose. The great flames and crimson smoke, which at night had appeared so dazzling, sank into insignificance. If anyone has the temerity to doubt the existence of a gracious, mighty God, let him stand at sunrise on the top of Asamayama and behold the wonder of His works!

I hardly dared to breathe for fear I would dispel the illusion, but a hearty lunch eaten with the edge of the crater for a table, made things seem pretty real. The coming down was fearful for the ashes were very deep, and we often went in up to our knees.

The next morning at eleven, I rolled into my bed more dead than alive. My face and hands were blistered from the heat and the ashes, and I was sore from head to foot, but I had a vision in my soul that can never be effaced.

The Lady of the Decoration

Well here I am back in H. (I used to think it stood for that too but it does n't!) Curiously enough I rather enjoy getting back into harness this year. Three kindergartens to attend in the morning, class work in the afternoon, four separate accounts to be kept, besides housekeeping, mothers' meetings, and prayer meetings, would have appalled me once.

The only thing that phases me is the company. If only some nice accommodating cyclone would come along and gather up all the floating population, and deposit it in a neat pile in some distant fence corner, I would be everlastingly grateful. One loving brother wrote last week that he was coming with a wife and three children to board

with us until his house was completed,
and that he knew I would be glad to
have them. Delighted I am sure! All
I need to complete my checkered career
is to keep a boarding-house! I
smacked Susie Damn clear down the
steps and sang "A consecrated cross-
eyed beau," then I wrote him to come,
It is against the principles of the school
to refuse anyone its hospitality, con-
sequently everybody who is out of a
job comes to see us.

The waves of my wrath break upon
Miss Lessing for allowing herself to
be imposed upon, but she is as calm
and serene as the Great Buddha of
Kamakura.

My special grievance this morning is
cooked tomatoes and baby organs.
Our cook has just discovered cooked
tomatoes, and they seem to fill some
longfelt want in his soul. In spite of

protest, he serves them to us for breakfast, tiffin and dinner, and the household sits with injured countenance, and silently holds me responsible. As for the nine and one wind bags that begin their wheezing and squeaking before breakfast, my thoughts are unfit for publication! This morning I was awakened by the strains " Shall we meet beyond the River? " Well if we do, the keys will fly that 's all there is about it! Once in a while they sidetrack it to " Oh! to be nothing, nothing!" That is where I fully agree and if they would only give me a chance I would grant their desire in less time than it takes to write it. I am sure my Hades will be a hard seat in a lonesome corner where I must listen to baby organs all day and live on a perpetual diet of cooked tomatoes.

To-day they are bringing in the

wounded soldiers from Liaoyang, and I try to keep away from the windows so I will not see them. Those bright strong boys that left here such a little while ago, are coming back on stretchers, crippled and disfigured for life.

Yesterday while taking a walk, I saw about two hundred men, right off the transport, waiting for the doctors and nurses to come. Men whose clothes had not been changed for weeks, ragged, bloody and soiled beyond conception. Wounded, tired, sick, with almost every trace of the human gone out of their faces, they sat or lay on the ground waiting to be cared for. Most of the wounds had not been touched since they were hastily tied up on the battlefield. I thought I had some idea of what war meant, but I had n't the faintest conception of the real horror of it.

The Lady of the Decoration

Miss Lessing is trying to get permission for us to do regular visiting at the hospitals, but the officials are very cautious about allowing any foreigner behind the scenes.

Just here I hung my head out of the window to ask the cook what time it was. He called back, "Me no know! clock him gone to sleep. He no talk some more."

I think I shall follow the example of the clock.

HIROSHIMA, October, 1904.

Dearest Mate:

I have been to the hospital at last and I can think of nothing, see nothing, and talk of nothing but those poor battered up men. Yesterday the authorities sent word that if the foreign teachers would come and make a little music for the sick men it would be appreciated. We had no musical instrument except the organ, so Miss Lessing and I bundled one up on a jinrikisha and trudged along beside it through the street. I got almost hysterical over our absurd appearance, and pretended that Miss Lessing was the organ grinder, and I the monkey. But oh! Mate when we got to the hospital all the silliness was knocked out of me. Thousands of mutilated and dying men, literally shot to pieces by the Russian bullets. I can't talk about it! It was too horrible to describe.

We wheeled the organ into one of the wards and two of the teachers sang while I played. It was pitiful to see how eager the men were to hear. The room was so big that those in the back begged to be moved closer, so the little nurses carried the convalescent ones forward on their backs.

The Lady of the Decoration

For one hour I pumped away on that wheezy little old instrument, with the tears running down my cheeks most of the time. So long as I live I 'll never make fun of a baby organ again. The joy that one gave that afternoon justified its being.

And then—prepare for the worst,— we distributed tracts. Oh! yes I did it too, in spite of all the fun I have made, and would you believe it? those men who were able to walk, crowded around and *begged* for them, and the others in the beds held out their hands or followed us wistfully with their eyes. They were so crazy for something to read that they were even willing to read about the foreign God.

It was late when we got back and I went straight to bed and indulged in a chill. All the horror of war had come home to me for the first time, and my very soul rebelled against it. They say you get hardened to the sights after a few visits to the hospital, but I hope I shall never get to the point of believing that it's right for strong useful men to be killed or crippled for life in order to settle a controversy.

Before we went into the wards the physician in charge took us all over the buildings, showed us where the old bandages were being washed and cleaned, where the instruments were sharpened and repaired, where the stretchers and crutches, and "first aid to the injured" satchels were kept. We were taken through the postoffice, where all the mail comes and goes from the front. It was touching to see the number of letters that had been sent home unopened.

Twenty thousand sick soldiers are cared for in Hiroshima, and such system, such cleanliness and order you have never seen. I have wished for Jack a thousand times; it would delight his soul to see the skill and ability of these wonderful little doctors and nurses.

HIROSHIMA, November, 1904.

To-morrow it will be four weeks since I have had any kind of mail from America. It seems to me that everything has stopped running across the ocean, even the waves.

I know little these days outside of the kindergarten and the hospital. The former grows cuter and dearer all the time. It is a constant inspiration to see the daily development of these cunning babies. As for the visits to the hospital, they are a self-appointed task that grows no easier through repetition. You know how I shrink from

187

seeing pain, and how all my life I have tried to get away from the disagreeable? Well it is like torture to go day after day into the midst of the most terrible suffering. But in view of the bigger things of life, the tremendous struggle going on so near, the agony of the sick and wounded, the suffering of the women and children, my own little qualms get lost in the shuffle, and my one consuming desire is to help in any way I can.

Last week we took in addition to the "wind bag" two big baskets of flowers to give to the sickest ones. Oh! If I could only make you know what flowers mean to them! Men too sick to raise their heads and often dying, will stretch out their hands for a flower, and be perfectly content to hold it in their fingers. One soldier with both arms gone asked me for a flower just as I had emptied my basket. I would have given my month's salary for one rose, but all I had was a withered little pansy. He motioned for me to give him that and asked me to put it in a broken bottle hanging on the wall, so he could see it.

If I did n't get away from it all once in a while, I don't believe I could stand it. Yesterday was the Emperor's birthday and we had a holiday. I took several of the girls and went for a long ramble in the country. The fields were a brilliant yellow, rich and heavy with the unharvested wheat. The mountains were deeply purple, and the sky so tenderly blue, that the whole world just seemed a place to be glad and happy in. Fall in Japan does not suggest death and decay, but rather the drifting into a beautiful rest, where dreams can be dreamed and the world forgot. Such a spirit of peace enveloped the whole scene, that it was hard to realize that the long line of black objects on the distant road were stretchers bearing the sick and wounded from the transports to the hospitals.

HIROSHIMA, December, 1904.

Last Saturday I had to go across the bay to visit one of our branch kindergartens. Many Russian prisoners are stationed on the island and I was tremendously interested in the good time they were having. The Japanese officials are entertaining them violently with concerts, picnics, etc. Imagine a lot of these big muscular men being sent on an all-day excursion with two little Japanese guards. Of course, it is practically impossible for the men

to escape from the island but I don't
believe they want to. A cook has actually been brought from Vladivostock
so that they may have Russian food,
and the best things in the markets are
sent to them. The prisoners I saw
seemed in high spirits, and were having as much fun as a lot of school boys
out on a lark. I don't wonder! It is
lots more comfortable being a prisoner
in Japan than a soldier in Manchuria.

I only had a few minutes to visit the
hospital, but I was glad I went. As
the doctor took me through one of the
wards where the sickest men lay, I saw
one big rough looking Russian with
such a scowl on his face that I hardly
dared offer him my small posy. But
I hated to pass him by so I ventured
to lay it on the foot of the cot. What
was my consternation when, after one
glance, he clasped both hands over his

face and sobbed like a sick child. "Are you in pain?" asked the doctor. "No," he said shortly, "I'm homesick." Oh! Mate, that finished me! Did n't I know better than anybody in the world how he felt? I just sat down on the side of the cot and patted him, and tried to tell him how sorry I was though he could hardly understand a word.

This morning I could have done a song and dance when I heard that he had been operated on and was to be sent home.

Almost every day we are having grand military funerals, and they are most impressive I can tell you. Yesterday twenty-two officers were buried at the same time, and the school stood on the street for over an hour to do them honor. The procession was very interesting, with the Buddhist

The Lady of the Decoration

priests, in their gorgeous robes, and the mourners in white or light blue. First came the square box with the cremated remains, then the officer's horse, then coolies carrying small trees which were to be planted on the grave. Next came a large picture of the deceased, and perhaps his coat or sword, next the shaven priests in magnificent raiment and last the mourners carrying small trays with rice cakes, to be placed upon the grave. The wives and mothers and daughters rode in jinrikishas, hand folded meekly in hand, and eyes downcast. Such calm resigned faces I have never seen, many white and wasted with sorrow, but under absolute control. Of the entire number only one gave vent to her grief; a bent old woman with thin grey hair cut close to her head, rode with both hands over her face. She had lost two sons in one battle, and the cry of her human heart was stronger than any precept of her religion.

HIROSHIMA, December, 1904.

You remember the Irishman's saying that we could be pretty comfortable in life if it was n't for our pleasures? Well I could get along rather well in Japan were it not for the Merry Christmases. Such a terrible longing seizes me for my loved ones and for God's country that I feel like a needle near a magnet. But next Christmas! I just go right up in the air when I think about it.

This school of life is a difficult one at best, but when a weak sister like myself is put about three grades higher than she belongs, it is more than hard. I don't care a rap for the struggle and the heart aches, if I have only made good. When I came out there were two kindergartens, now there are nine besides a big training class. Anybody else could have done as much for the work but one thing is certain, the work could n't have done for anyone else what it has done for me. Outwardly I am the same featherweight as of old, but there is a big change inside, Mate, you 'll have to take my word for it. I am coming to take the slaps of Fate very much as I used to take the curling of my hair with a hot iron, it pulled and sometimes burned, but I did n't care so long as it was going to improve my looks. So now I use my crosses as sort of curling irons for my character.

Your sudden decision to give up your trip to Europe this spring set me guessing! I can't imagine, after all

195

your planning and your dreams, what could have changed your mind so completely. You don't seem to care a rap about going. Now look here, Mate, I want a full report. You have turned all the pockets of my confidence inside out. What about yours? Have you been getting an "aim" in life, are you going to be an operatic singer, or a temperance lecturer, or anything like that? You are so horribly high minded that I am prepared for the worst.

I wish it would stop raining. The mountains are hid by a heavy gray mist, and the drip, drip of the rain from roof and trees is not a cheering sound. I am doing my best to keep things bright within, I have built a big fire in my grate, and in my heart I have lighted all the lamps at my little shrines, and I am burning incense to the loves that were and are.

196

The Lady of the Decoration

Just after tiffin the rain stopped for a little while and I rushed out for a walk. I had been reading the "Christmas Carol" all morning, and it brought so many memories of home that I was feeling rather wobbly. My walk set me up immensely. A baldheaded, toothless old man stopped me and asked me where I was "coming." When I told him he said that was wonderful and he hoped I would have a good time. A woman with a child on her back ran out and stopped me to ask if I would please let the baby see my hair. Half a dozen children and two dogs followed me all the way, and an old man and woman leaned against a wall and laughed aloud because a foreigner was so funny to look at.

If anyone thinks that he can indulge in a nice private case of the blues while taking a walk in Japan, he de-

ceives himself. I started out feeling
like Napoleon at St. Helena, and I
came home cheerful and ravenously
hungry.

I have been trying to read poetry
this winter, but I don't make much
progress. The truth is I have gained
five pounds, and I am afraid I am getting too fat. I never knew but one fat
person to appreciate poetry and he
crocheted tidies.

By the way I have learned to knit!!
You see there are so many times when
I have to play the gracious hostess
when I feel like a volcano within, that
I decided to get something on which
I could vent my restlessness. It is as-
tonishing how much bad temper one
can knit into a garment. I don't know
yet what mine is going to be, probably
an opera bonnet for Susie Damn.

The Lady of the Decoration

You are not any more surprised to hear from me in Kyoto than I am to be here. One of the teachers here, a great big-hearted splendid woman, knowing that I was interested in the sick soldiers, asked me to come up for a week and help the Red Cross nurses. For six days we have met all the trains, and given hot tea, and books to both the men who were going to the front and to those who were being brought home. We work side by side with Buddhist priests, ladies of rank, and coolies, serving from one to four hundred men in fifteen minutes! You never saw such a scrimmage, everybody works like mad while the train stops, and the wild "Banzais" that

199

greet us as the men catch sight of the hot tea, show us how welcome it is.

But the sights, Mate dear, are enough to break one's heart. I have seen good-byes, and partings until I have n't an emotion left! One man I talked with was going back for the fourth time having been wounded and sent home again and again; his wife never took her eyes from his face until the train pulled out, and the smile with which she sent him away was more heart rending than any tears I ever saw.

Then I have been touched by an old man and his wife who for four days have met every train to tell their only son good-bye. They are so feeble that they have to be helped up and down the steps and as each train comes and goes and their boy is not on board, they totter hand in hand back to the street corner to wait more long hours.

Going one way the trains carry the soldiers to the front, boys for the most part wild with enthusiasm, high spirits, and courage, and coming the other way in vastly greater numbers are the silent trains bearing the sick and wounded and dead.

We meet five trains during the day and one at two in the night. I have gotten so that I can sleep sitting upright on a hard bench between trains. Think of the plucky little Japanese women who have done this ever since the beginning of the war!

Out of my experience at the station came another very charming one yesterday. It seems that the president of the Red Cross Society is a royal princess, first cousin indeed to the Emperor. She had heard of me through her secretary and of the small services I had rendered here and at Hiroshima, so she requested an interview that she might thank me in person.

It seemed very ridiculous that I should receive formal recognition for pouring tea and handing out posies, but I was crazy to see the Princess, so early yesterday morning, I donned my best raiment and sallied forth with an interpreter.

The house was a regular Chinese puzzle and I was passed on from one person to another until I got positively dizzy. At last we came to a long beautiful room, at the end of which, in a robe of purple and gold, all covered with white chrysanthemums, sat the royal lady. I was preparing to make my lowest bow, when, to my astonishment, she came forward with extended hand and spoke to me in English! Then she bowled me right over in the first round by asking me about Kindergarten. I forgot that she was a lady of royalty and numerous decorations, and that etiquette forbade me speaking except when spoken to. She was so responsive and so interested, that I found myself talking in a blue streak. Then she told me a bit of her story, and I longed to hear more. It seems that certain women of the royal line are not permitted to marry, and she, being restless and ambitious, became a Buddhist Priestess, having her own temple, priestesses, etc. The priestesses are all young girls, and I wish you could have seen them examining my clothes, my hair and my rings. The Princess herself is a woman of brilliant attainments, and fine executive ability.

Of course we had tea, and sat on the floor and chattered and laughed like a lot of school girls. When I left I was told that the Princess desired my photograph at once, and that I should sit for it the next day. I suppose I am in for it.

HIROSHIMA, December, 1904.

My dearest Mate:

The American mail is in and the secret is out, or at least half-way out and I am wild with curiosity and interest. You say you can't give me any of the particulars and you would rather I would n't even guess. All that you want me to know is that you have "a new interest in life that is the deepest and most beautiful experience you have ever known." I will do as you request, not ask any questions, or make any surmises but you will let me say this, that no fame, no glory, no wealth can ever give one thousandth part of

the real heart's content that one hour
of love can give. Without it work of
any kind is against the full tide, and
accomplishment is emptier than vanity.
The heart still cries out for its own,
for what is its birthright and heritage.

I am glad with all my soul for your
happiness, Mate, the tenderest bless-
ing that lips could frame would not express half that is in my heart. There
is nothing so sure in life as that love
is best of all. You think you know it
after a few weeks of loving, I know
I know after years of grief and suffering and despair.

From the time when you used to
stand between me and childish punish-
ments, through all the happy days of
girlhood, the sorrowful days of womanhood, on up to the bitter-sweet present,
you have never failed me.

I want to give you a whole heart full

of gladness and rejoicing, I want to crowd out my own little wail of bereavement, but Oh! Mate, I never felt so alone in my life before! I am not asking you to tell me who the man is. I am trying not to *guess*. Tell me what you like and when you like, and rest assured that whatever comes, my heart is with you—and with him.

HIROSHIMA, January, 1905.

It has been longer than usual since I wrote but somehow things have been going wrong with me of late and I did n't want to bother you. But oh! Mate, I have n't anybody else in the world to come to, and you 'll have to forgive me for bringing a cloud across your happiness.

The whole truth is I 'm worsted! The fight has been too much. Days, weeks, months of homesickness have piled up on top of me until all my courage and my control, all my *will* seem paralysed.

Night after night I lie awake and stare out into the dark, and staring back at me is the one word *"alone"*. In the daytime, I try to keep somebody with me all the time, I have gotten afraid of myself. My face in the mirror does not seem to belong to me, it is a curious unfamiliar face that I do not know. Every once in a while I want to beat the air and scream, but I don't do it. I clench my fists and set my teeth and teach, teach, teach.

But I can't go on like this forever! Flesh and spirit rebel against a lifetime of it! Have n't I paid my penalty? Are n't the lightness and brightness and beauty ever coming back?

On my desk is a contract waiting to

be signed for another four years at the school. Beside it is a letter from Brother, begging me to drop everything and come home at once. Can you guess what the temptation is? On the one hand ceaseless work, uncongenial surroundings and exile, on the other luxury, loved ones,—and dependence. I must give my answer to-morrow and Heaven only knows what it will be. One thing is certain I am tired of doing hard things, I am tired of being brave.

It is storming fearfully but I am going out to mail this letter. If I cable that I am coming you must be the first one to know why. I have tried to grow into something higher and better, God knows I have, but I am afraid I am a house built on the sands after all. Don't be hard on me, Mate, whatever comes remember I have tried.

The Lady of the Decoration

If you open this letter first, don't read the one that comes in the same mail. I wrote it this afternoon, and I would give everything I possess to get it back again. When I went out to mail it, I was feeling so utterly desperate that I did n't care a rap for the storm or anything else. I went on and on until I came to the sea-wall that makes a big curve out into the sea. When I had gone as far as I dared, I climbed up on an old stone lantern, and let the spray and the rain beat on my face. The wind was whipping the waves into a perfect fury, and pounding them against the wall at my feet. The thunder rolled and roared, and great flashes of lightning ripped gashes in the green and purple water. It was the most glorious sight I ever saw! I felt that the wind, the waves, and the storm were all my friends and that they were doing all my beating and screaming for me.

I clung to the lantern, with my clothes dripping and my hair streaming about my face until the storm was over. And I don't think I was ever so near to God in my life as when the sun came out suddenly from the clouds and lit up that tempest-tossed sea into a perfect glory of light and color! And the peace had come into my heart, Mate, and I knew that I was going to take up my cross again and bear it bravely. I was so glad, so thankful that I could scarcely keep my feet on the ground. I struck out at full speed along the sea wall and ran every step of the way home.

And now after a hot bath and dry

clothes, with my little kettle singing by my side, I want to tell you that I have decided to stay, perhaps for five months, perhaps for five years.

Out of the wreckage of my old life I've managed to build a fairly respectable craft. It has taken me just four years to realize that it is not a pleasure boat. To-night I realize once for all that it is a very modest little tug, and wherever it can tow anything or anybody into harbor there it belongs, and there it stays.

Tell them all that I am quite well again, Mate, and as for you, please don't even bother your blessed head about me again. I have meekly taken my place in the middle of the sea-saw and I shall probably never go very high or very low again. I am sleepy for the first time in two weeks, so goodbye comrade mine and God bless you.

The Lady of the Decoration

HIROSHIMA, February, 1905.

My dearest Mate:

I can't feel quite right until I tell you that I have guessed your secret, that I have known from the first it was Jack. I always knew you were made for each other, both so splendid and noble and true. It is n't any particular credit to you two that you are good, there was no alternative—you could n't be bad.

How perfectly you will fit into all his plans and ambitions! A beautiful new life is opening up for you, a life so full of promise, of tremendous possibilities for good not only for you but for others that it seems like a bit of heaven.

Tell him how I feel, Mate. It is

hard for me to write letters these days, but I want him to know that I am glad because he is happy.

I have been living in the past to-day going over the old days in the Mountains up at the lake, and the reunions on the farm. How many have gone down into the great silence since then! Somehow I seem nearer to them than I do to you who are alive. While I am still on the crowded highway of life, yet I am surrounded by strange, unloving faces that have no connection with the joys or the sorrows of the past.

How the view changes as we pass along the great road. At first only the hilltops are visible, rosy and radiant under the enthusiasm of youth, then the level plains come into sight flooded with the bright light of mid-day, then slowly we slip into the valleys where the long shadows fall like memories across our hearts.

Oh! well, with all the struggles, all the heartaches, I am glad, Mate, very glad that I have lived—and laughed. For I am laughing again, in spite of the fact that my courage got fuddled and took the wrong road.

I heard of a man the other day who had received a sentence of fifteen years for some criminal act. He was in love with the freedom of life, he was young and strong, so he made a dash down a long iron staircase, dropped into a river, swam a mile and gained his freedom. All search failed to find him, but two days later he walked into the police station and gave himself up to serve his time. I made my dash for liberty, but I have come back to serve my time.

I don't have to tell you, Mate, that

214

The Lady of the Decoration

I am ashamed of having shown the white feather. You will write me a beautiful letter and explain it all away, but I know in my soul you are disappointed in me, and to even think about it is like going down in a swift elevator. Being able to go under gracefully is my highest ambition at present, but try as I will, I kick a few kicks before I disappear.

Please, please, Mate, don't worry about me. I promise that if I reach the real limit I will cable for a special steamer to be sent for me. But I don't intend to reach it, or at least I am going to get on the other side of it, so there will be no further danger.

Two long months will pass before I get an answer to this. It will come in April with the cherry blossoms and the spring.

The Lady of the Decoration

You must forgive me if the letters have been few and far between lately. After my little "wobble" I plunged into work with might and main, and I am still at it for all I am worth. First I house-cleaned, and the old place must certainly be surprised at its transformation. Fresh curtains, new paper, cozy window seats, and bright cushions have made a vast difference. Then I tackled the kindergarten, and the result is about the prettiest thing in Japan. The room is painted white with buff walls and soft muslin curtains, the only decoration being a hundred blessed babies, in gay little kimonas, who look like big bunches of flowers placed in a wreath upon the floor.

216

The Lady of the Decoration

As for my training class, I have no words to express my gratification. I can scarcely believe that the fine, capable, earnest young women that are going out to all parts of Japan to start new Kindergartens, are the timid, giggling, dependent little creatures that came to me four years ago.

Goodness knows I was as immature in my way as they were in theirs, but in my desperate need, I builded better than I knew. I recklessly followed your advice and hitched my little go-cart to a star, and the star turned into a meteor and is now whizzing through space getting bigger and stronger all the time, and I am tied on to the end of it unable to stop it or myself.

If I only had more sense and more ability, think what I might have done!

The work at the hospital is still very heavy. The wards are bare and repellant and the days are long and dreary for the sick men. We do all we can to cheer them up, have phonograph concerts, magic lantern shows, with the magic missing, and baby organ recitals. The results are often ludicrous, but the appreciation of the men for our slightest effort is so hearty that it more than repays us.

I saw one man yesterday who had gone crazy on the battlefield. He looked like a terror stricken animal afraid of everybody, and hiding under the sheet at the slightest approach. When I came in he cowered back against the wall shaking from head to foot. I put a big bunch of flowers on the bed, and in a flash his hands were stretched out for them, and a smile came to his lips. After that whenever I passed the door, he would shout out,

"Arigato! Arigato!" which the nurse said was the first sign of sanity he had shown.

In the next room was a man who had fallen from a mast on one of the flag ships. He had landed full on his face and the result was too fearful to describe. The nurse said he could not live through the night so I laid my flowers on his bed and was slipping out when he called to me. His whole head was covered with bandages except his mouth and one eye, and I had to lean down very close to understand what he said. What do you suppose he wanted? To look at my hat!! He had never seen one before and he was just like a child in his curiosity.

Of course, as foreigners, we always excite comment, and are gazed at, examined and talked about continually.

The Lady of the Decoration

I sometimes feel like a wild animal in a cage straight from the heart of Africa!

Our unfailing point of contact is the flowers. You cannot imagine how they love them. I have seen men holding them tenderly in their fingers and talking to them as they would to children. Imagine retreating soldiers after a hard day's fight, stopping to put a flower in a dead comrade's hand!

Oh! Mate, the most comical things and the most tragic, the most horrible and the most beautiful are all mixed up together. Every time I go to the hospital I am faced with my wasted years of opportunities. It takes so little to bring sunshine and cheer, and yet millions of us go chasing our own little desires through life, and never stop to think of the ones who are down.

No, I am not going to turn Missionary nor Salvation Army lassie, but with God's help I shall serve some-where and "good cheer for the lonely" shall be my watch-word.

I am lots better than I was, though I am still tussling with insomnia. My crazy nerves play me all sorts of tricks, but praise be I have stopped worrying. I have come at last to see that God has found even a small broken instrument like myself worth working through, and I just lift up my heart to Him every day, battered and bruised as it is, in deep unspeakable thankfulness.

HIROSHIMA, April, 1905.

My dearest Mate:

Your letter is here and I have n't a grain of sense, nor dignity, nor anything else except a wild desire to hug everything in sight! I am having as many thrills as a surcharged electric battery, and I am so hysterically happy that I don't care what I do or say.

Why did n't you tell me at first it was Dr. Leet? My mind was so full of Jack that I forgot that other men inhabited the earth. It is no use bluffing any longer, Mate, there has never been a minute since the train pulled out of the home station that every instinct in me has n't cried out for Jack. Pride kept me silent at first, and then the miserable thought got hold of me that he was beginning to care for you. Oh! the agony I have suffered, trying to be loyal to you, to be generous to him, and to put myself out of the question! And now your blessed letter comes, and laughs at my fears and says "Jack chooses his wife as he does his friends, for eternity."

The Lady of the Decoration

I have no words to fit the occasion, all I can say is now that happiness has shown me the back of her head I am scared to death to look her in the face. But I "shore do" like the arrangement of her back hair.

Don't breathe a word of what I have written, but as you love me find out absolutely and beyond all possibility of doubt if Jack feels exactly as he did four years ago. If you give me your word of honor that he does, then—I will write.

I have signed a contract for another year, and I must stay it out, but I would spend a year in Hades if Heaven was at the end of it.

All you say about Dr. Leet fills me with joy. He does not need any higher commendation in this world nor the next than that you are willing to marry him! Is n't it dandy that he is going to back the hospital scheme?

The Lady of the Decoration

When I think of the way Jack has worked for ten years without a vacation, putting all his magnificent ability, his strength, his youth, his health even into that project, I don't wonder that men like Dr. Leet are eager to put their money and services at his disposal. You say Dr. Leet does it upon the condition that Jack takes a rest. Make him stick to it, Mate, he will kill himself if he is n't stopped.

I have read your letters over and over and traced your love affair every inch of the way. Why are you such an old clam? To think that I am the only one that knows your secret, and that up to to-day I have been barking up the wrong tree! Never mind, I forgive you, I forgive everybody, I am drunk with happiness and generous in consequence.

My little old lane is glorified, even

the barbed wire fence on either side
scintillates. The house is too small, I
am going out on the River Road, and
see the cherry blossoms on the hill
sides and the sunlight on the water,
and feel the road under my feet. I
feel like a prospector who has struck
gold. Whatever comes of it all, for
this one day I am going to give full
rein to my fancy and be gloriously
happy once more.

HIROSHIMA, May, 1905.

There is a big yellow bee, doing the
buzzing act in the sunshine on my window, and I am just wondering who is
doing the most buzzing, he or I? His
nose is yellow with pollen from some
flower he has robbed, his body is fat
and lazy, all in all he is about the happiest bee I ever beheld. But I can go

him one better, while it is only his wings that are beating with happiness, it is my heart that is going to the **tune** of rag-time jigs and triumphal alleluias all at the same time.

My chef, four feet two, remarked this morning "Sensei happy all same like chicken!" He meant bird, but any old fowl will do.

Oh! Mate, it is good to be alive these days. For weeks we have had nothing but glorious sunrises, gorgeous sunsets, and perfect noondays. The wistaria has come before the cherry blossoms have quite gone, and the earth is a glow of purple and pink with the blue sky above as tender as love.

Each morning I open my windows to the east to see the marvel of a new day coming fresh from the hands of its Maker, and each evening I stand at the opposite window and watch the same day drop over the mountains to eternity. In the flaming sky where so often hangs the silver crescent is always the promise of another day, another chance to begin anew.

Just one more year and I will be turning the gladdest face homeward that ever a lonely pilgrim faced the West with. There will be many a pang at leaving Japan, I have learned life's deepest lesson here, and the loneliness and isolation that have been so hard to bear have revealed inner depths of which I never dreamed before. What strange things human beings are! Our very crosses get dear after we have carried them awhile!

I have had three offers to sign fresh contracts, Nagasaki, Tokyo, and here, but I am leaving things to shape themselves for the future. Whatever happens I am coming home first. If happiness is waiting for me, I 'll meet it with out-stretched arms, if not I am coming back to my post. Thank God I am sure of myself at last!

The work at the hospital this month is much lighter, and the patients are leaving for home daily. The talk of peace is in the air, and we are praying with all our hearts that it may come. Nobody but those who have seen with their own eyes can know the unspeakable horrors of this war. It is not only those who are fighting at the front who have known the full tragedy, it is those also who are fighting at home the relentless foe of poverty, sickness, and desolation. If victory comes to Japan, half the glory must be for those silent heroic little women, who gave their all, then took up the man's burden and cheerfully bore it to the end.

The Lady of the Decoration

I was very much interested in your account of the young missionary who is coming through Japan on her way to China. I know just how she will feel when she steps off the steamer and finds no friendly face to welcome her. I talked over your little scheme with Miss Lessing and she says I can go up to Yokohamo in July to meet her and bring her right down here. Tell her to tie her handkerchief around her arm so I will know her, and not to worry the least bit, that I will take care of her and treat her like one of my own family.

Can you guess how eagerly I am waiting for your answer to my April letter? It cannot come before the last of June, and happy as I am, the time seems very long. Yet I would rather live to the last of my days like this, travelling ever toward the pot of gold at the end of the rainbow, than ever to arrive and find the gold not there!

You say that at last you know I am the "captain of my soul." Well, Mate, I believe I am, but I just want to say that it's a hard worked captain that I am, and if anybody wants the job—very much—I think he can get it.

YOKOHAMA, July 5, 1905.

Do you suppose, if people could, they would write letters as soon as they got to Heaven? I don't know where to begin nor what to say. The only thing about me that is on earth is this pen point, the rest is floating around in a diamond-studded, rose-colored mist!

I will try to be sensible and give you some idea of what has been happening, but how I am to get it on paper I don't know. I got here yesterday, the 4th of July, on the early train, and rushed down to the hatoba to meet the launch when it came in from the steamer. I had had no breakfast and was as nervous as a witch. Your letter had not come, and my fears were increasing every moment.

Well I took my place on the steps as the launch landed and waited, with very little interest I must confess, for your young missionary to appear. By and by I saw a handkerchief tied to a sleeve, but it was a man's sleeve. I gave one more look, and my heart seemed to stop. "Jack!" I cried, and then everything went black before me, and I did n't know anything more. It was the first time I ever fainted; sorrow and grief never knocked me out, but joy like that was enough to kill me!

When I came to, I was at the hotel and I did n't dare open my eyes. I knew it was all a dream, and I did not want to come back to reality. I lay there holding on to the vision, until I heard a man's voice close by say, "She will be all right now, I will take care of her." Then I opened my eyes, and with three Japanese maids and four Japanese men and two ladies off the steamer looking on, I flung my arms about Jack's neck and cried down his collar!

He made me stay quiet all morning, and just before tiffin he calmly informed me that he had made all the arrangements for us to be married at three o'clock. I declared I could n't, that I had signed a contract for another year at Hiroshima, that Miss Lessing would think I was crazy, that I must make some plans. But you know Jack! He met every objection that I could offer, said he would see Miss Lessing and make it all right about the contract, that I was too nervous to teach any more, and last that I owed him a little consideration after four years of waiting. Then I realized how the lines had deepened in his face, and how the grey was streaking his hair, and I surrendered promptly.

We were married in a little English church on the Bluff, with half a dozen witnesses. Several Americans whom Jack had met on the steamer, a missionary friend of mine, and the Japanese clerk constituted the audience.

It is all like a beautiful dream to me still, and I am afraid to let Jack get out of my sight for fear I will wake up. It was Fourth of July, and Christmas, and birthday, and wedding

day all rolled into one. The whole city
was celebrating, the hotel a flutter of
flags and ribbons, the bay full of every
kind of pleasure craft. At night there
was a grand lantern fete and fire-
works, and a huge figure of Uncle
Sam with stars in his coat tails.
Thousands of Japanese in their gayest
kimonas thronged the Bund, listening
to the music, watching the foreigners
and the fire-works.

Jack and I were like two children,
he forgot that he was a staid doctor,
and I forgot that I had ever been
a Foreign Missionary Kindergarten
teacher. We were boy and girl again
and up to our eyes in love. It was
the first Fourth of July for fifteen
years that I did not have some unhap-
piness to conceal. As one of my girls
said about herself: "My little lonely
heart had flewed away!"

The Lady of the Decoration

All the loneliness, the heartaches, the pains are justified now. I do not regret the past for through it the present is.

Do you remember the lines: "He shall restore the years that the locust hath eaten?" Well I believe that while I have been struggling out here, He has restored them, and that I will be permitted to return to a new life, a life given back by God.

Of course you know we are going on around. It seems rather inconsistent to say I am glad of it after all my wailing for home. The truth is, home has come to *me*!

Jack says we are to meet you and Dr. Leet in Paris. You need n't try to persuade me that Heaven will be any better than the present!

There is no use in my trying to thank you for your part in all this, dear Mate. I have been in a chronic state of gratitude to you ever since I was born! I can only say with all my heart and soul "God bless you and Good-bye."

P.S. In my wedding ring is engraved M.L.O.T.D. Can you guess what it means?